CHRISTMAS

The Nativity

CHRISTMAS

A COLLECTION OF CHRISTMASLORE

by

JOHN N. THEN

THE BRUCE PUBLISHING COMPANY
MILWAUKEE

Dedicated

to

The Christ Child

Whose Birth Christmas Commemorates

FOREWORD

The material for this book of Christmaslore was gathered over a period of many years, from all available sources — much of it from foreign lands. Hence, the writer makes no claim of originality or authority for it. It is merely a collection of legends, traditions, folklore, stories, fancies, customs, etc., entwined around Christmas and Christmas celebrations, religious and otherwise.

It is possible that some of the legends contradict others on the same subject. If so, the reader must keep in mind that they are purely folklore, and must be considered as such. It may be noted further, that many of the customs and quaint notions mentioned are now antiquated.

The reader himself must estimate the value of this collection. However, if the book implants in the reader's heart a deeper reverence for the feast of Christmas, if it gives him pleasure or help of any kind, the object of its writing is accomplished.

To all who in any way assisted me in gathering this material, my thanks.

"Glory to God in the highest, and on earth peace to men of good will."

JOHN N. THEN

Hastings, Minnesota

CONTENTS

PART FOUR — CAROLS AND POEMS

APPENDIX

[xii]

PART ONE

The Christmas Cycle

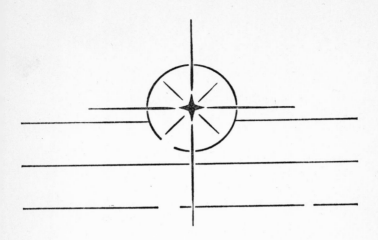

THE NATIVITY

The Annunciation

Intimately connected with the Nativity is the Annunciation to the Virgin Mary by the Archangel Gabriel. "Hail full of grace, the Lord is with thee," etc.; to which she replied, "Be it done unto me according to thy word." An Italian legend says that Gabriel was accompanied by a host of lower angels anxious to behold their queen; these, however, remained at the door while he entered.

The Marriage of Joseph and Mary

Mention of the marriage of Joseph and Mary should be included with the Nativity and Holy Family narratives. Until she was fourteen years old, Mary lived in the temple with other virgins under the charge of pious matrons.

[5]

They were occupied with embroidery for the temple hangings and vestments of the priests. An angel having come to Zacharias, the high priest, informed him of the destiny of Mary and told him to call together all the widowers among the people and let each bring his rod, and he to whom the Lord should give a sign, should be the husband of Mary. Joseph the carpenter, a righteous man, appeared with his staff in hand before the priest with the rest. As he presented his staff, a dove, white as snow, issued out of it and after settling on his head, flew toward heaven. Then the priest said to him, "Thou art the person chosen to take the Virgin of the Lord and to keep her for Him." So Joseph took her to his house in Nazareth.

Another tradition cites that various suitors aspiring to the honor of marrying the "Virgin of the Lord" deposited their wands in the temple during the night and the next morning the rod of Joseph was found to have budded forth into leaves and lilylike flowers. The other suitors thereupon broke their wands in despair.

It is not determined how old Joseph was at this time. Early pictures represent him as a very old man, but, with better taste and more propriety, he is represented in later pictures as a man of about fifty, still strong and robust and able to work at his trade and defend Mary and provide for her and her divine offspring.

The Wedding Dress of Mary and Joseph

From legends, traditions, and visions, some very unusual as well as interesting details of the wedding dress of Mary and Joseph are recorded. Mary's parents, Joachim and Anna, were well-to-do people, although Joachim was no longer living when the marriage took place. The wedding was celebrated in Jerusalem in a house near Mount

Sion which was frequently let for similar occasions, and according to custom, the festivities lasted for seven or eight days. Besides the witnesses and companions of Mary in the school of the temple, there were many relatives present.

The marriage was solemn and sumptuous. Many lambs were killed and offered in sacrifice. Mary's bridal dress, which Anna had bought for her, was a very large gown open in the front, with large sleeves. This gown had a blue ground strewn with red, white, and yellow roses, intermingled with green leaves; the lower border was trimmed with fringe and tassels. Over her dress she wore a mantle of celestial blue terminating in a train. In her left hand she carried a crown of red and white roses, made of silk, while in her right hand was held a gilt candlestick. Out of humility Mary would not consent to wear the dress after the ceremony. She had an abundance of hair of a bright hazel brown color over which she wore a white veil with a crown placed over it. Afterwards she put on a dress less splendid. It was the custom for rich people to change their dress three or four times for their marriage.

Joseph had on a wide robe of blue with very large sleeves, and round his neck he wore a brown collar with two white bands hanging down over his breast. Then, as now, a wedding ring was used, and Joseph placed one on the finger of the Virgin Mary. Mary's wedding ring is preserved in a church in Perouse, Italy, where it is exhibited to the people on August 3 of each year.

Preparations for the Birth of Jesus

It is related that Anna, the mother of the Virgin Mary, was not poor, and that she helped Mary prepare articles which might be used at the birth of her Babe. She got ready coverlets, bandages, and swaddling clothes as she believed the event would take place at her house and that all her relatives would visit her on this occasion. Among the articles was a coverlet with figures and sentences worked by the needle and interwoven with threads of gold. In the middle was a sort of wrapper in which to place the woman. When the different parts of the coverlet were fitted together around her with strings and buttons, she could easily sit up between the cushions and receive the visits of her friends who would sit around her on the border of the tapestry.

Anna was very busy and much concerned regarding all these preparations when an angel appeared to Joseph and told him to depart with Mary to Bethlehem, for it was there she should bring her Child into the world. The angel directed what he should take with him; that he should take but few things and especially not the embroidered coverlet. Anna was much distressed but the Virgin Mary knew by the text of the prophecies that the Saviour would be born in Bethlehem and conformed to the Divine Will. When the angel appeared to Joseph and told him to depart for Bethlehem he instructed him to take besides the ass on which Mary would ride, another ass a year old who had no young, and to let it run at liberty and always follow the road it took. This ass was brought from Anna's pasture, and while on the journey it ran sometimes in advance, and sometimes close to the travelers. They followed the young ass which always took crossroads and did not go into cities. When the road was well defined, it often ran a long way before them, but when it divided, the young ass waited and took the right direction. When they desired to stop, it stopped of itself. In this way the young ass led them on. It was the eve of a Sabbath day and they found themselves at the dwelling of some shepherds* who received them kindly.

Joseph and Mary observed the Sabbath and rested all day, receiving visits from a number of people with their children who had conceived an affection for the Blessed Virgin. Joseph and his host took a walk in the vicinity, as was done by the country people on the Sabbath day, while Mary spoke to the women and children. She endeared herself so much to the women that they begged her to remain with them, offering all assistance and friendship and showed compassion on her tender state. But the Holy Family resumed their journey, making frequent halts, always following the young ass and arriving at last at Bethlehem.† Here the young ass ran around the city as Joseph sought shelter for the night, only to be rebuffed with "no room in the inn." They went from house to house and always suffered refusal. As they arrived at the grotto, the young ass, which had run around the city, came to meet them and began joyfully to leap about near them.

From this sign they knew that the grotto was to be their resting place, and Joseph cleared away many things which partially obstructed the entrance. Here they remained for the night, and the next day Joseph went to Bethlehem to buy some things they required. It was the second night they spent at the grotto when the birth of our Saviour took place. The young ass had continued very joyfully and played about the shed, before the grotto where Joseph had fastened him.

---

*Subsequently the daughters of these people married servants of the three kings who remained in Palestine.

† The distance from Nazareth to Bethlehem is about seventy-six miles.

The Birth of Christ

Within the grotto, Joseph was seized with a holy fear and prostrated himself with his face to the ground while Mary was praying on her knees. A light surrounded her and became more and more brilliant until midnight when Mary was transported in an ecstasy. She was raised from the ground, her hands crossed upon her breast. The rock which formed the floor and the walls of the grotto seemed alive with light. A luminous path went from Mary to heaven. The Blessed Virgin turned her eyes to the feeble newborn Infant of whom she had become the mother, lying before her on the ground. The brilliance of the Child eclipsed all the surrounding splendor. The Holy Mother remained some time in ecstasy, then wrapped the Child in linen cloth and took Him in her arms while angels surrounded them. Joseph was still praying with his face to the ground. An hour elapsed after the birth of the Child, before he rose, and full of joy and humility received the Infant Jesus in his arms. They then placed the Infant in the crib. Mary was neither ill nor fatigued.

The Place Where Christ Was Born

It is believed the stable where Christ was born was the interior of a cavern still shown in Bethlehem. In front of the stable was a ruined house once inhabited by Jesse, the father of David, and near the spot where David pastured his sheep, but the house was now a partly thatched shed and open to all the bitter winds. Here it was that the Blessed Virgin brought forth her first-born Son, wrapped Him in swaddling clothes and laid Him in a manger. One old legend relates that Joseph went to seek a midwife with whom he returned to the stable. When they entered it was filled with light and they beheld Mary sitting there with the Infant at her bosom, and the woman being amazed said "Can this be true?" and Mary answered, "It is true; as there is no Child like unto my Son, so there is no woman like unto His mother." The ox and ass which were in the stable at the time of Christ's birth are regarded as symbols — the ox an emblem of the Jews; the ass, of the Gentiles. It has often been told in song and story that the ox and ass kept the newborn Infant warm with their breaths on that wintry night.

Legend of Straw and Hay

A beautiful legend of Christmas tells that when the Virgin Mary bound up her Infant Son with swaddling clothes and laid Him in the manger, the dry straw and hay with which it was filled were restored to freshness and life, and beautiful wild flowers formed themselves into a wreath which twined around the head of the Divine Babe. Among the straw there was also some dry fern which alone felt too proud and lazy to awaken, and showed no sign of joy nor reverence to the newborn King. As a punishment, the fern was for all time deprived of its blooming flowers and must forever stand erect and alone in the dark places of the forest, whereas at one time it was privileged to bear silver flowers and grew in the sunshine.

Animals

That animals in both stable and forest fall on their knees in adoration on midnight of Christmas Eve, and that many animals, especially horses and pigs, have human tongues with which to prophesy for the coming year, is a belief of many European peasants. There is a story told in the German Alps of a servant who did not believe that animals had the power of speech at midnight on Christmas and mocked at the idea of it being unlucky to overhear them. He wanted to satisfy himself so hid himself in a stable on Christmas Eve and at midnight he heard one horse say: "We shall have hard work this day week." The other replied: "And the way to the churchyard is long and steep." The unbelieving man knew then that it was his own death which was foretold, and in truth he was buried that day week.

Why the Cattle Kneel when They Lie Down ⌘

At the birth of the Divine Babe, the ox fell on its knees in adoration and ever after it was privileged to kneel before lying down, while other animals do not.

The Blacksmith ⌘ ⌘

As Joseph and Mary were seeking shelter for the night and found no place in the inn, they passed a blacksmith who was at work hammering a piece of white-hot iron. Pitifully the strangers asked if they could not obtain lodging for the night and roughly the answer came that he had no place for them. "Be on your way," said he, "I am too busy to be bothered," and he hammered away.

"And what are you doing," meekly asked the tired and heartsore woman.

"Making nails to crucify the Messias who is to be born soon," was the rough reply.

The shades of night were falling and Joseph and Mary journeyed on until they came to the stable where they sought shelter and where Mary gave birth to her first-born Child. As the morning dawned, there came silently and alone, a young girl who entered the stable. She was the daughter of the blacksmith. "Come and see the Christ

Child," was Mary's greeting to the girl. "That I can never do, for I am blind," said the girl as she burst into tears. Mary told the poor girl to touch the crib and the Child within and assured her she would regain her sight. This the girl did, and immediately her bright eyes beheld the light and she saw again.

So happy was she that she forgot all about the mother and Child in the manger and ran home to tell her father of the miracle that had befallen her. The father embraced his child and asked how it came about. As the daughter told him it was the lovely lady who asked him for shelter the night before, he left his work and hastened to the stable where he knelt before the Holy Mother and Child and begged their pardon. "Oh, if I had only known that you were to be the mother of God, I would have given you my own bed and I would have slept on the stone floor," gasped the blacksmith as the tears rolled down his face. Mary spoke kindly to him and told him to arise and go in peace. The blacksmith lived long years after and plied his trade but made only horseshoes and keys and hammered no more on the nails to crucify the Messias.

The Nightingale

The Holy Mother delighted to sing her Baby to sleep. She sang of the angels as the Christ Child cuddled to her breast. But one evening He seemed restless and her song failed to lull Him to sleep. A little bird which had nested on the roof and listened to the Virgin's song fluttered in and perched on her shoulder and began to sing as though his little throat must burst, and the Child fell asleep. Then the bird stopped singing and gently pressed his little beak against the ear of the Virgin Mother as though he wanted to kiss her. She petted the bird lovingly and whispered: "Little bird, you shall henceforth carry my voice in you and know all my songs, you shall have the sweetest song of all the birds. Fly away now and sing." To this day, when it is time to rock the little ones to sleep, the nightingale's silver voice is heard; meanwhile the streams flow softer and the leaves of the trees stop their fluttering and all the birds and animals are silent to listen to the song that lulled the Christ Child to sleep.

Why the Robin's Breast is Red

As the Christ Child lay in the manger one day, the scant fire that had been built to keep Him warm was slowly dying out. A little robin seeing this, hopped up to the fire and began flapping its wings to fan it back to burning. Patiently and untiringly he fluttered his little wings and the fire became brighter and brighter so that even the feathers of the little breast of the bird radiated the glow thereof and became red, remaining so ever after.

The Egg Dent

The Christ Child was hungry and His Mother had nothing to give Him but a single egg which was offered to her by a poor woman. The Holy Mother began preparing the egg for her hungry Babe, but first with a little spoon she dipped out a bit of the white part and gave it to Him to taste. This tasted so good to the Child that the Mother never failed after that to dip a small portion of the white of the egg and lovingly reach it to Him. Since then, one finds in every egg a little dent, which is the portion the Holy Mother gave to the Christ Child who relished it so much.

A Lamb Conceals the Christ Child

The message that Christ was born spread fast and wide throughout the land. Herod, the king, was much alarmed and exceedingly jealous because he was told that the new-born Babe was hailed as the "King" of kings. He ordered all infants under two years old to be massacred, thinking in this way that the newborn Christ would be among them. Terrible it was to hear the heart-rending cries of the mothers as their babes were torn from their bosoms and brutally slaughtered. Although the murderers slew thousands of innocent children, they were not positive that the sought-for Christ Child was one of them. To satisfy himself, therefore, Herod ordered some hirelings to return and thoroughly search the stable where the Babe was born. Stealthily they approached and looking through a crack in the wooden door, beheld a Child in the manger within. They forced the door open and rushed in, but the Child was gone. A frightened lamb ran across the straw. "What is this?" said they. "Did we not see the Child with our own eyes?" and they turned the straw over a hundred times and looked under the roof and in every nook and corner. The Child had disappeared. "What became of it?" As the murderous soldiers of Herod neared the stable, there was great confusion and noise. Joseph and Mary were hurriedly making what arrangements they possibly could to flee to Egypt. The Babe in the manger, too, was disturbed and slipped out. A little lamb near by seemed to understand it all and quietly came over to the Christ Child bleating "I will hide You" and gently covered Him like a canopy while the heavenly Babe clung fast to the long white fleece beneath. Just then the soldiers burst open the door of the stable and began their search for the Babe, which they had seen as they peeked through the crack a few moments before. But in vain was their search, for no sooner had they entered, than the lamb with his precious burden passed them unnoticed and went out. And so the Christ Child was saved from the wrath of Herod.

THE SHEPHERDS*

The Shepherd's Fire

It was cold and the newborn Christ Child was lying in the manger. St. Joseph was much alarmed and hurried to look about for some source of warmth. There was no light save the radiant stars above, which shone brightly. "Perhaps I can find a fire at the shepherds on the hillside," thought St. Joseph, as he hurried across the field, and indeed, there, afar off, he could see some glowing coals. Hastily he approached the spot and found three shepherds and a dog, watching their sheep. The shepherds could not understand why the dog did not bark or try to bite the stranger; on the contrary, he wagged his tail in a most joyful manner. "What is it you want?" asked one of the shepherds. St. Joseph came nearer and asked for a bit of the fire to warm his Child that was just born. "If that's all you want," said the oldest shepherd, "then help yourself." "But wherein will you carry it?" asked the younger one. St. Joseph took off his mantle and piled the burning wood on the cloth which he laid on the

*According to an old legend, Simon and Jude, afterwards apostles, were among the shepherds who came to adore the newborn Babe at Bethlehem on Christmas morning.

ground. As he departed, the shepherds wondered how it was the mantle did not burn.

At this time something strange happened. A shower of stars appeared from the heavens and an angel stood before the shepherds and told them to hasten to the stable where their fire was brightly burning. "There you will find a Babe wrapped in swaddling clothes, lying on straw in a manger, and beside Him, His blessed mother and father, the man you were following even now. Rejoice for this Child is the Messias, Halleluja" and the angel disappeared.

The legs of the excited shepherds moved of their own accord and they were on their way to the stable. As they crossed the field, they looked into their knapsacks to see if they had anything to bring to the heavenly Child. One found a cheese that was white and fresh; the second had a dove in his sack, and the third rejoiced because he caught a rabbit by the ears. So they came to the stable and found all as the angel had announced, while St. Joseph knelt beside the manger, blowing the fire which he had brought in the mantle.

The Glowworm

A little beetle nestled on the roof of the stable in Bethlehem just as the angel announced the glad tidings of the birth of Christ to the shepherds. He wished he could make known to all the animals what had happened. He flew to the angel, who was greatly pleased, and from his shimmery hair the angel took a tiny spark which he placed between the wings of the beetle. The spot on the beetle shone like a glowing diamond and he flew from bush to bush and tree to tree. All the animals, big and little, the birds and butterflies, and even the worms and insects marveled at the light the beetle carried in the dark and they understood his message. Returning to the stable where Mary and Joseph watched over the Christ Child, the beetle darted about so they could see and he did so until dawn appeared. From that day to this, he is called glowworm, so says the legend.

The Daisy

Among the shepherds who watched the sheep, as the angel appeared and announced the birth of Christ, was a small boy who had to do all sorts of menial tasks for his elders. As the rest of the shepherds went to Bethlehem, this little fellow was told to take care of the fire and watch the potatoes that were baking in the hot ashes, lest they be burnt. Sadly he watched the shepherds cross the field until he could see them no longer, when he, too, determined to go, and putting a fresh supply of wood on the fire, he stole forth in the night to the stable. Silently he entered and saw the heavenly Babe lying in the manger and surrounded with light. The shepherds all brought gifts, but he had nothing to give. Should he return and get some of the baked potatoes for a gift or perhaps the sheep pelt he used as a bed to sleep upon, or — and a thought entered his mind. He left and hurried to the field where he had this day found a tiny white daisy that had pushed its head above the snow, as if it, too, wished to see what had happened.

Without any trouble he found the flower and picked it and brought it to the Christ Child, who took it in His little hands and touched it to His mouth. There, where the Babe's lip touched the flower, a crown of yellow glorified it, and the daisy wears this crown from that day to this.

The Shepherd's Feather Tick   ✄

Once upon a time there was a shepherd who slept on a warm feather tick. Awakening one night, he thought of the poor Christ Child lying on a handful of straw in the cold, hard manger. He hardly knew whether it was real or a dream. It impressed him so. "This is a great injustice for me to lay on a warm, soft bed of feathers while the Christ Child has only straw in a cold, hard manger," the shepherd rebuked himself. Quickly he arose and took his feather tick on his shoulder to bring it to the Christ Child. As he crossed a field, an angel suddenly appeared to him and said, "Fear not, my good man, when the Christ Child suffers from the cold, He does it for the love of you and all mankind. As a reward for your act of kindness to the Christ Child, you will one day sit at the side of Jesus in heaven and when the Christ Child's birthday dawns, you are privileged to scatter the feathers from your bed upon the earth below."

So, when the snow comes dancing down on Christmas, everyone can tell that the shepherd is scattering the feathers of his bed, and the trees and forests and fields are sleeping in peace and warmth under the blanket of white that flutters like feathers from heaven.

The Little Gray Lamb   ✄   ✄

Among the flocks of the shepherds on the hillside of Bethlehem was a single gray lamb. This little lamb wished to be white like the others and often gazed at the stars and asked them to give him a fleece of white, but they could not, neither could the clouds with all their fleecy whiteness change his color from gray to white, nor could the trees do anything to help the matter.

At the time the shepherds went to the stable at Bethlehem, the sheep went too, and so did the little gray lamb. They went into the stable to see the Christ Child, all but the gray lamb which stayed outside because he had no white fleece.

The little Christ Child blessed the shepherds and the sheep, then looking up He saw the gray lamb and asked him to come in too. The little gray lamb came in, and the Christ Child put His hand on the lamb's head and blessed him. "The Babe's loving touch so light, had changed the fleece from gray to white."

It is said that the sheep go in procession in commemoration of the visit of the angel to the shepherds.

THE MAGI

The Journey of the Wise Men

Tradition calls the three Wise Men, Melchior, Balthasar, and Caspar. In art they are depicted as a very old man, a middle-aged man, and a young man, and coming from different races. Although of different nations, their kingdoms bordered on each other and tradition represents that they would meet from time to time to discuss matters of mutual interest, especially their astronomical findings, for they were devoted students of the heavenly bodies, hence their title, "wise men." In their contact with the Jews, they had learned of the prophesies saying that a luminous star would announce salvation to the world.

They watched and studied the skies, hoping to discover the object of their desires. No sooner did it appear in the heavens than they all set forth to find and adore Him who was destined to save the world and to offer Him their hearts and rich gifts.

Babylon, Melchior's capital, was chosen for the starting place. Preparations were made and princes and nearest kin were permitted to accompany them. They made the journey on camels, escorted by a numerous retinue of servants and attendants carrying necessary provisions.

The Wise Men knew that it was to Judea that they must go. The star was leading them to its capital, Jerusalem. To their surprise, the closer they got to Jerusalem, the more the guiding star waned, and as they entered the city, it disappeared completely. The people of that city marveled at the strangers. They sought the palace of the king, confident that he would be able to guide them in their quest. King Herod was not in a good mood. He was angry because of the reports that in the city of Bethlehem a Babe had been born, at whose birth the angels sang messages of joy and peace to men of good will. The priests and soothsayers tried to quiet the king, attributing the strange report to the hallucination of a few shepherds who claimed to have heard the singing of angels.

Herod wanted to believe this version of the story, yet he could not help worrying. He pretended great interest in the narration of the Magi concerning the star and its significance, yet excused himself from joining their party. Nevertheless he urged them to return by way of Jerusalem, telling him what they had found, so that he, too, might go and adore the much-heralded King. Bidding him farewell, the Magi started off. No sooner had they left the suburbs of Jerusalem, when the guiding star appeared once more and brighter than ever. They proceeded by a roundabout way, guided by the star, until they came to a cave on the outskirts of Bethlehem. The brightness of the star illuminated the surroundings, and entering the cavelike grotto they beheld the Virgin Mother, and in a manger the Christ Child, while Joseph stood watching. Mary, inspired with the significance of the visit of the Magi, presented the Divine Child to them, while they, on bended knees, presented their homage and veneration together with their gifts of gold, frankincense, and myrrh. At the same time they placed their scepters at His feet in recognition of His divine authority. Warned by an angel in a vision, they did not return to Herod as they had intended, because Herod was plotting to kill the Babe and had malicious intents against the Wise Men themselves. St. Joseph likewise was warned in a dream of the dangers from the envious Herod. They would flee to Egypt for safety while the Magi were to return to their native countries by a different route.

Concerning the Magi

There are authorities who claim that when the Magi reached Jerusalem and inquired of King Herod regarding the place of birth of the newborn King, Herod directed them to Bethlehem to the north. They did not have the star to guide them as they went north into the Holy Land, nor upon their return to Jerusalem, after discovering that nothing had happened in the Bethlehem to the north. On reaching Jerusalem, the star reappeared. They followed it, not to Bethlehem, but it led them directly to Egypt, since the flight had already taken place and that when the Magi reached the place where Christ was, the Babe must have been over a year old, because He could walk and was led by Mary to the Wise Men who still carried their gifts. Early paintings, sculptures, and mosaics represent the Child Jesus as about two years old when the Magi came. It is an undecided point whether the adoration of the Magi took place thirteen days or one year and thirteen days after the birth of Christ.

Tradition says that they were visited in after years by St. Thomas the Apostle, who baptized them and elevated them to the holy priesthood and later they were made bishops.

[24]

Magi Gifts

The gifts of the Magi were symbolical of their three-fold faith; the gold that He was King; the incense that He was God; and myrrh, that He was man and doomed to death. The Virgin bestowed on the Magi gifts of the linen bands in which she had wrapped the Saviour, for which they thanked her in great humility, and laid them among their treasures. According to the old legends, Caspar is king of Tarsus, the land of merchants; he makes the offering of gold. Melchior, the king of Arabia and Nubia, offers frankincense, and Balthasar, king of Saba, "the land of spices," offers myrrh.

The Gift of Bethlehem

For twenty-four months the Magi traveled together and the time of separation for Caspar had come. Watching Melchior and Balthasar proceed, he waited until he could see them no longer, then turned homeward. His thoughts were now of the home and family he had left two years ago and it was yet a two-day ride before he could reach them. He yearned for Ilzaide, his wife, and their son who would now be twelve years old, almost a man. Caspar rode steadily, and without mishap he entered the gates of his native city at sundown of the second day. The heavens were resplendent with brilliant colors of crimson-gold and purple of the sunset, and he took it for a happy omen. "Only a few paces more thou faithful Haboul," he cries to his horse, "and we are home." A moment later he was in the courtyard but no servants came to the gate. He pushed the gate open, and entered. All seemed deserted. Then a sound of far-off wailing greeted his ears.

With fear in his heart, Caspar hurried down the corridor which led to the living rooms of his family. The wailing grew louder and he saw that it came from the servants huddled together at the entrance to one of the rooms. From them he learned that his son lay dying within the room. Caspar pushed aside the heavy silken hangings and stepped into the room. Lights were burning and the boy lay dying on a couch piled high with cushions, while the mother with clasped hands knelt by his side watching him. Caspar drew near but she did not raise her eyes. "Thou art in time to see thy boy die," said she. Falling on his knees, Caspar wept and took the boy's hand in his. "Why didst thou go? and hast thou found the King?" she asked idly, her eyes fixed on the boy's face. "Yea, we found Him, we adored and at His feet was laid our gifts of gold, frankincense, and myrrh." "And what gave this new King in return, no amulet whose touch would bring back life." "He had naught to give, He was divine." "Divine indeed!" she cried scornfully. "If this be true, then He could cure our child. Hast thou nothing that the King has touched?" "Nothing save this," and Caspar reluctantly drew from his bosom a small piece of linen. She took it and mockingly replied: "It is the linen poor women spin for their children's clothes." "I begged the linen from His mother, for it had covered the royal head of the Babe and she gave it to me gladly," and Caspar broke in despair. "They call thee wise," said Ilzaide bitterly, "but I think thou art a fool. Can a piece of linen cure my child? See, I throw thy precious rag away." In her excitement the precious cloth fell from her hand on the body of the boy. As the linen touched it, the boy who had lain motionless for hours, moved, a shudder ran through his body, and he opened his eyes, and smiled — virtue had come from the clothing of the King. "I was wrong. If thou hadst not followed the star our son had died," wept Ilzaide. "Oh, blessed star, whose shining has brought such joy into this house." "The star," repeated Caspar, and his gaze grew fixed. While for a moment, in place of his son on the couch, he saw the little Babe in far-away Bethlehem wrappend in swaddling clothes and laid in a manger.

The Fire Worshipers

A curious myth relates that after the Magi offered their gifts to the newborn King in the stable of Bethlehem, He raised His little hands and broke a piece from the rock manger in which He lay. This He offered to them and they accepted it. As the Magi started their return journey and wanted to take the small piece of stone along, it proved to be so heavy in weight that they could not lift it, neither could their horses and camels move it. The Wise Men said to one another: "Of what use is this piece of stone anyway? it is of no value." With united effort and strength they rolled the stone over the edge of a cistern which was near by. No sooner had the stone sunk in the depths of the water, when a lightninglike fire gushed forth. Immediately they realized that the Giver of the stone was a Mighty God and they regretted exceedingly what they had done. From the fire, however, each one of them took a portion along and carried it burning to his native land where it was worshiped. The cistern is still pointed out to travelers and it is said if one looks into the deep thereof, with a pure heart, he can see the fire flash over the water. Others maintain that it is the reflection of the star which, after it had fulfilled its mission of directing the Wise Men to the Holy City, sank in this cistern.

The Three Kings' Cake

As the Magi were journeying to Bethlehem, they arrived at a small town in Judea just at nightfall. They stopped at the first house and asked for shelter for the night. The house belonged to a Jew named Ismael who had a hard time to support his wife and children. "I have only one bed and can give you only bread and olives to eat and milk to drink. If that will satisfy you, I beg you to enter," said Ismael. They entered and were given to eat and were left to rest in the only bed, while Ismael and his family slept on straw. The following morning before they left, Balthasar told Ismael that they were three kings and wanted to reward him in a kingly way for his hospitality. "Here is gold for you, and besides we will buy the finest house in town for you," to which the Jew replied, "I did not expect any pay, my heart prompted the deed," as he held out his hand to accept the gift. The kings found a handsome house richly furnished and carpeted which they bought and gave to the poor man. "Use your wealth wisely and be especially considerate of the poor," they admonished him and promised to call on him again on their return from Bethlehem to learn how he had acted. Bidding him farewell, they continued their journey.

Ismael soon forgot his former rank and the advice of his benefactors. He spread a great feast and invited all the prominent people of the town to it. He and his wife were dressed lavishly. So as not be disturbed at the feast, Ismael commanded the servants to drive away any beggars who might call, and he even placed two sentinels armed with clubs at the gate to ward off any intruders. It happened that on this same evening the three kings returned from Bethlehem where they had offered their gifts to the Christ Child. They saw the house of Ismael all lighted up and decided to find out how he had kept his promise to be considerate of the poor people. Disguised as beggars, they approached the house, but were driven away by the servants. Ismael himself happened to see them through an open window and shouted "Away with you, beggars," and he let the dogs loose, one of which bit Caspar in the leg. "This man does not deserve what was given him," said Melchior. "We will drive him out of his paradise." Within, the feast went on merrily and Ismael was just about to cut a huge cake, when a commotion was heard. The three kings in resplendent robes and crowns on their heads were at the gate. Ismael saw them through the same open window and hurried out to greet them with many bows and pressed them with invitations to come in. "Thank you," said Balthasar dryly, "we cannot accept anything from a man who is so hard-hearted toward the poor." "You have kept your promise very well indeed," said Melchior. "You turned the dogs on the beggars," said Caspar. "Return to your former position and be a beggar again yourself, that is what you have earned." At the signal of the kings, the servants drove Ismael and his wife and children out of the house. Since that time people cut a generous piece of cake for the poor before they offer any to their guests on Christmas.

Mosaic of the Magi On the Basilica of the Nativity in Bethlehem

In 614 the Persians invaded the Holy Land and ransacked the holy places. After devastating the holy sanctuaries in Jerusalem, they came to Bethlehem. Arriving at the Basilica of the Nativity they beheld on the façade of the building, a brilliant mosaic representing the Magi, dressed in Persian costume adoring the Christ Child. They pondered over the matter and, wondering if the place was not under their protection, they hesitated and passed by without plundering the shrine.

The Magi in Art

It is interesting to note that it was not until the fifteenth century that one of the Magi is represented as a negro. As early as the sixth century they had the title of kings which is generally used today, but they were not pictured with crowns until after the eleventh century. In treating the subject of the Magi the following rule is now followed: Melchior is a venerable old man with long beard and hair, who offers a gift of gold as a subject doing homage to his King. Caspar, a ruddy and beardless youth, offers incense, as a creature adoring his God. Balthasar in middle life, swarthy and bearded, offers the embalming spice of myrrh. Thus they represent the three stages of human life — youth, middle life, and old age, and the three great divisions of the human family, Asiatic, European, and African.

Bodies of the Magi

The bodies of the Magi were brought from Persia by order of the Empress Helena and were venerated at Constantinople, but were later transferred to Milan. When Frederick Barbarossa conquered Milan, he bequeathed the precious relics to the bishop of Cologne, and in the year 1164 they were brought to that city with great pomp and joy. There they rest to this day in the world-famous cathedral.

Cistern of the Wise Men

About halfway from Jerusalem to Bethlehem is a spring called to this day the Cistern of the Wise Men, where tradition says the Magi, being weary in their search for the Infant King and losing sight of the star, sat down to rest, and then saw the reflection of it in the water. It was also the resting place of Mary on her way to Bethlehem.

Ships of Tarsus

A curious legend relates that when Herod found that the three kings had escaped from him in the ships of Tarsus, in his wrath he burned all the vessels in the port.

Ages of the Magi

According to tradition, Caspar lived to be 109 years old, Melchior 116 years, and Balthasar 110 years.

The Thirty Pieces of Silver

A curious legend connecting the Nativity with the Passion of our Lord is as follows: Among the gifts offered by the Magi to the Holy Infant were thirty pieces of silver. When the Holy Family fled to Egypt the Virgin Mary took the coins with her but lost them. They were found by a shepherd who was a leper. He kept the money until the day he was cured of his leprosy by Christ at Jerusalem. In his gratitude the shepherd offered the thirty pieces of silver as a gift to the temple and the priests afterwards gave them to Judas as the price of Christ's betrayal.

THE FLIGHT INTO EGYPT

The Route Followed

It is supposed that Joseph traveled from Bethlehem across the hilly country of Judea taking the road to Joppa and then pursuing the way along the coast. It was a journey of at least 400 miles, which must have occupied five or six weeks.

Aspen

A legend relates that as the Holy Family were on their flight into Egypt, they entered a thick forest. In reverence to the Infant, all the trees bowed themselves down except the aspen, which in her pride stood upright. Then the Infant pronounced a curse against her, and at the sound of His words the aspen began to tremble through all her leaves, and has not ceased to tremble even to this day.

The Leprous Child

While on their journey, the Holy Family, one night, saw a lantern hanging on a tree beside a cabin which was surrounded by ditches. The cabin was the abode of robbers and the lantern had been hung up to attract travelers. When the Holy Family reached the lantern, several of the robbers met them intending to rob and perhaps kill them. A ray of light emanating from the Christ Child struck

[32]

the heart of the chief and he ordered the other robbers to do no harm to the travelers. He then led the Holy Family into his cabin in which were his wife and two children, who appeared timid. When the saintly travelers had finished eating the provisions which they had brought them, Mary requested some water to bathe her Child. This she did and also washed His swaddling clothes and hung them before the fire to dry. The robber was so touched that he told his wife to ask the Mother for permission to bathe their little leprous child in the same water, thinking it might perhaps cure it. When the woman approached her, Mary told her, before the woman spoke, to bathe the leprous child in this water. No sooner had the infant been dipped in it, than the scales of his leprosy came off and he was cured. These people and their companions were greatly astonished and showed great respect to the Holy Family who remained for the night, departing in the early morning, accompanied for some distance by the robbers who led them to a safe road. As they took leave of the Holy Family, the chief said, "Remember us in whatever place you go."

And it came to pass that at the scene of the crucifixion the good thief, who said, "Remember me when Thou comest into Thy kingdom," was none other than the infant cured of leprosy.

Robbers

There is an ancient tradition that when the Holy Family were descending into the plains of Syria they encountered two thieves. One of them would have maltreated them, but his comrade interfered and said, "Suffer them to go in peace, and I will give thee forty groats and my girdle." The offer was accepted and the merciful robber led the Holy Family to his hut and gave them lodging for the night. On departing, Mary said to him: "The Lord will grant thee pardon for thy sins and receive thee to His right hand," and it was so — for in after times, these two thieves were crucified with Christ, one at the right and one at the left, and the merciful thief went with the Saviour into Paradise. The scene of this encounter with the robbers is still pointed out to travelers.

Palm Tree

One of the most popular legends concerning the flight into Egypt is that of the palm and date tree, which at the command of Jesus bowed down its branches to shade and refresh His mother.

The Kind Husbandman

A pretty legend is told of the Holy Family pursued by Herod's soldiers while on their flight to Egypt. Passing a field where a man was sowing corn, the Virgin said to the sower, "If anyone asks you whether we have passed this way, ye shall answer: 'Such persons passed this way when I was sowing this grain.'" The Holy Virgin was too wise and too good to save her Son by instructing the man to tell a falsehood, and by the power of the Infant Saviour in the space of a single night the seed sprung up and was fit for the sickle. The next morning the officers of Herod came up and inquired of the husbandman saying, "Have you seen an old man with a woman and a Child traveling this way?" and the man who was reaping his grain replied, "Yes, when I was sowing this corn." Then the officers of Herod turned back and left off pursuing the Holy Family.

Hazel Bush

While on their flight to Egypt, the Holy Family, pursued by the soldiers of Herod, were overtaken by a terrific storm. Lightning flashed and thunder crashed while they had no shelter other than a hazel bush which grew near. All about lightning struck and the soldiers of Herod fled in fear, but the hazel bush that sheltered the Holy Ones was unharmed and untouched. Since then it is said that the hazel bush is a safe protection against lightning, and whoever seeks shelter under one during a storm will be guarded. Another legend of the hazel bush is as follows: The Holy Mother was one day picking strawberries when a poisonous snake almost bit her. Having nothing with which to kill it but a hazel branch that grew near, Mary struck the serpent with it and the poisonous snake lay lifeless at her feet. The hazel bush has never lost this wonder power and its strike is sure to slay any poisonous reptile.

Yeast

Pursued by Herod's soldiers, the Holy Family reached a house where the woman was kneading bread. The Christ Child was in great peril and the Blessed Mother asked the woman to hide Him for her. The wicked soldiers had already reached the entrance and there was not a moment to lose. Quickly the good woman took the Holy Babe and placed Him in the dough and kept on as though she was mixing her bread. Entering the room, the soldiers searched from top to bottom, in closets, and trunks, and even the oven of the stove was not overlooked. Disappointed in their search, they departed. As the woman took the hidden Babe out of the dough and gave Him back safe to His mother, the dough seemed to rise and become light as sponge and there was no end to the amount of bread she baked from it. The news of this wonder spread quickly and all her neighbors came to beg a particle of the sponge to mix with their dough when they baked, and so it came that yeast is used to raise bread dough and multiplies seemingly without end.

Why the Ravens and Crows Are Black

Originally the ravens and crows were covered with snow-white plumage of which they were very proud. They would strut about and bathe and pluck their feathers from morning until night. One day while on their flight, the Holy Family came to a stream and, being very thirsty, they wanted a drink of the clear, cool water. The ravens and crows were bathing in this stream and on the approach of the Holy Family would roil and stir up the water until it became almost black so that the thirsty ones could not drink of it. As a punishment, these birds were changed from white to black and ever after all their kind are feathered with black instead of white as they at one time were, and they caw about it until this day.

Turtles

Another time as the Holy Family were closely pursued by Herod's soldiers, they arrived at a small stream which they had to cross. Wading into the water with her bare feet, the Holy Mother stepped on a fish, as the stream was seemingly alive with them. There were so many of them that it was difficult to cross. Commanding half the fish to leave the water and crawl on the ground, the Holy Family crossed the stream in comfort. The fish which left the water turned into turtles and while they live on land, they still maintain their instinct for the water and are found on the banks of streams and rivers where they can swim in the water as well as crawl on the ground.

The Fly and the Spider

As they were being pursued by Herod's soldiers, the Holy Family became very tired and sat down to rest. So exhausted were they that they fell asleep. Nearer and nearer approached the pursuers and the Holy Babe was in grave danger when a fly rested on Joseph's face and annoyed him until he awoke. Realizing their danger, he hurriedly awoke the Mother and Babe and they hid in a very small cave near by. As they were within, a spider began weaving its web back and forth, to and fro, across the opening. When the wicked soldiers arrived and saw the entrance covered with spider webs, they laughed and said to themselves: "Certainly no one could have gone in there for a long time or they would have broken the web." Being in great haste to find the object of their search, they passed by and the Holy Family were again safe.

The Apple and Pear Trees of Alexandria

As the Holy Family reached the outskirts of Alexandria on their flight, they were almost exhausted from the heat and had nothing to eat. The branches of a pear tree loaded with fruit hung over a wall on the one side, while those of an apple tree reached out from the opposite side of the way. The Holy Mother asked the owner of the pear tree for a single pear. In anger he told her to leave, as he had no pears for her. "Those are stones on the tree, you cannot eat them," said he. Not discouraged, Mary went to the owner of the apple tree to ask for an apple. "You are hungry?" said he. "I will shake the tree for you, help yourselves and take some along in your pack." The Virgin blessed his apple tree and henceforth it bore the choicest fruit to be found. Even to this day, the apples of Alexandria are renowned for their unexcelled flavor. But as the owner of the pear tree came to pick his fruit, he found the entire tree had turned into stone, not only the fruit but the trunk, and branches, and leaves as well. Visitors to Alexandria are still shown this pear tree turned to stone, on the outskirts of the city.

The Garden of Balm

It is related that the Holy Family finally rested after their long journey in the village of Matarea, six miles from Cairo, beyond the city of Heliopolis, and took up their residence in a grove of sycamore trees, where a miraculous fountain sprung up. It still exists and is called by the Arabs, "The Fountain of Mary." This district is called the "Garden of Balm." It was the custom of Mary to wash the swaddling clothes of her Infant in the water of the fountain, and from the perspiration of the Lord Jesus, so distributed by her, comes the balm of that vicinity.

Why the Sun Always Shines on Saturday

The Holy Mother had so many cares and worries for the safety of her Child that often pearls of tears would trickle down her cheeks. To conceal the tears from Joseph and the Child, she would dry her eyes with her veil which often became so moist that she was obliged to hang it in the sun to dry. It was her custom to always do this on a Saturday so her veil would have a fresh appearance on the Sabbath day, and Christ always made the sun shine on Saturdays, at least long enough to dry the Virgin's veil. Even now, though it rains on this day, some time or other the sun shines, if only for an instant, to remind people of the Virgin's tears.

PART TWO

Christmas Customs in Other Lands

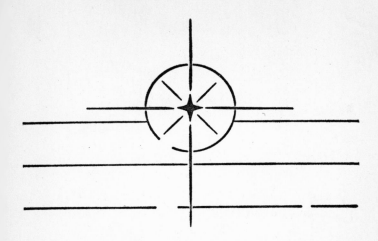

CHRISTMAS CUSTOMS IN OTHER LANDS

ALASKA

"Going round with the star" is a custom in which the Whites, Russians, and Indians of Alaska celebrate Christmas together. A star-shaped wooden frame is covered with bright tissue paper and for three nights is carried from door to door by boys and girls. Wherever they stop to sing carols, they are invited in and given something. On the third night another party of boys and girls, masked to represent Herod's soldiers, try to capture the star and destroy it, just as Herod's men tried to destroy the Infant Christ.

AUSTRALIA

Wonderful weather prevails in Australia at the Christmas season and the day is celebrated there with picnics and trips in the open.

AUSTRIA

In Austria great preparations are made for the Christmas festival. Two huge loaves of bread are baked typifying the Old and New Testaments. Three wax candles are especially made. On Christmas Eve one of the candles is lighted and the family sings a hymn. Before they begin to eat, the father takes the candle in his hand and says, "Christ is born." Then each child in turn takes the taper and standing on a stool repeats three times, "Praised be the Lord! Christ is born." The second candle is lighted on Christmas Day and the third on New Year's Day which ends the Christmas festivities.

BELGIUM

In Belgium, St. Nicholas goes from house to house on December 6, his feast day. He is followed by a black servant called Nicodemus (in Holland he is called *de swarte Pilt* — Black Pete). The saint is vested as a bishop and carries a gilded book in which to write the names of all good children. His servant carries a black book for the names of the bad children and also carries on his shoulders a huge black bag in which he is to carry away any naughty children. The children first recite their prayers and then ask for the toys they would like. They are told that St. Nicholas is expected from Spain, which is supposed to be his home. Young Belgian belles still take candles to the well at midnight to see the faces of their future husbands. It is feared in Belgium that if a light is extinguished accidentally on the table at the Christmas feast, some guest present will die in the course of the coming year.

CROATS AND SERBIANS

The Croats and Serbians give the Yule log a prominent place in their Christmas festivities. Before sunrise on Christmas morning, the men go to the forest and fell a tree, bringing it back in state. Lighted candles are placed on each side of the door through which it passes. It is wreathed with garlands, and corn and wine are sprinkled upon it. When it burns brightly, it is struck sharply with a rod, and as the sparks fly, wishes for the prosperity of the family are chanted.

CZECHOSLOVAKIA

In Czechoslovakia after the evening meal on Christmas Eve, fortunes are told. Melted wax or lead is poured into water and the future is told from the shapes it takes. Apples cut across to show a star of seeds also indicates coming events. Tiny candles are set upright in nutshells and floated in pans of water. The girl whose candle stays upright and burns to the end will have the best husband and live the longest.

Among the southern Slavs, if a girl is curious as to her future husband, she covers the table on Christmas Eve putting on a white loaf, a plate, knife, fork, and spoon. She then goes to bed. At midnight the spirit of her future husband will come and fling the knife at her. If it falls without hurting her, she will get a good husband, and be happy, and if she is hurt she will die early.

DENMARK

The Danish children do not have a Santa Claus but instead a Christmas brownie, called "Nisson," a little old man with a long gray beard who supposedly lives under the ground. The chief features of a Danish Christmas dinner are roast goose, rice, and apple fritters.

When the storks have left their nests in autumn, boat-loads of coarse brown crockery in the shape of little pigs with a slit in the back are brought to Denmark and bought by the children. They are savings banks and in these they drop their pennies which may not be taken out until the image is broken at Christmas time. At this season, too, the annual candle making occurs and is regarded as an occasion of great importance, as a goodly number are made especially for Christmas and are called Christmas Candles.

ENGLAND

The Yule Log

The Yule log was usually of oak and it was best to have it cut at midnight. The Yule log was dragged into the house with much ceremony. To help pull the log conferred immunity from witches. A bit of the log was always kept until the next Christmas to help kindle the new one, and this piece was believed to help shield the home against fire. While the Yule log was being lighted the following song was sung:

> Kindle the Christmas brand and then,
> Till sunset let it burne;
> Which quenched, then lay it up again,
> Till Christmas next return.
> Part must be kept wherewith to tend,
> The Christmas log next year;
> And where it is safely kept the fiend,
> Can do no mischief there.

Boar's Head and the Swan

The "Boar's Head" is given special prominence in many English dinners to commemorate the legend that a certain student of Queen's College, Oxford, being attacked by a boar on Christmas Day, choked the animal with a copy of Aristotle and took his head back for dinner. The swan also is sometimes seen on English tables as a dinner dish. They are especially fattened by giving them all the barley they can eat.

Bees

In some parts of England bees are popularly said to express their veneration for the nativity by singing, as it is called, in their hives at midnight on Christmas Eve.

Playing Cards

When playing cards were first introduced into England, they were looked upon purely as a Christmas pastime.

Spoons

In the seventeenth century it was the fashion in England to present the ladies of the household with a silver spoon at Christmas. It had quite a significance, as such spoons were often of considerable intrinsic value, being of rare and unusual pattern and exquisite finish.

Exposing of Grain

An early custom in England was the exposing of grain on Christmas night to gain fertility from the falling dew.

Christmas Tree

It was in 1840 that Queen Victoria and Prince Albert

had a Christmas tree and so it became fashionable in England.

"Still Christmas"

Carols were sung in England every year from time immemorial until in 1525, when the people were prohibited from singing them on account of the serious illness of the king. For this reason the Christmas of 1525 is remembered as the "Still Christmas."

"Wassail Bowl"

Wassail or Warsail bowl is regarded as of such antiquity that it is said to have been known by the ancient Britains. It has been a favorite Christmas beverage for centuries. An old recipe for "wassail" as it used to be made at Oxford is as follows: Put into a bowl half a pint of sugar, pour on it half a pint of warm beer; grate a nutmeg and some ginger into it; add four glasses of sherry and five additional pints of beer; stir it well; sweeten it to your taste; let it stand covered up for two or three hours, then put three or four slices of bread cut thin and toasted brown into it, and it is fit for use.

Twelfth-Night

Epiphany, or the twelfth night after Christmas, is often referred to as "Little Christmas." It was on that day that the Magi are supposed to have arrived with their gifts and adored the newborn King. In olden times, "Twelfth-night" revels were held in England. An invariable feature of this celebration was the great "Twelfth-night Cake" lit by a number of white candles. Within this cake were baked a bean and a pea. Whoever found the bean, if a man, was entitled to be king, while a pea entitled its lady possessor to be queen, of the party. Then followed the medieval custom of raising the king on the shoulders of four men to the ceiling where he chalked a cross on the rafters to keep away evil spirits. These revelries were presided over by the make-believe "King and Queen" seated on an improvised throne. Mock trials took place and scenes from English history enacted, and so forth. Merrily the time was thus spent until midnight when the Christmas greens which decorated the room were gathered and burned to close the festivities.

FINLAND

Father Christmas is dressed as a "yule goat" in Finland, when he distributes gifts on Christmas Eve. All receive gifts, including the dog who is given a large package securely tied like the rest of the gifts, containing a large piece of meat. After the gifts have been distributed, the children prepare to go to bed on the straw-covered floor in memory of the Christ Child born in the manger.

FRANCE

In France only the children have gifts. In some parts of France a youth, dressed in white and a crown set around with many little wax candles, represents the Christ Child. He carries a bell and a basket full of goodies. Accompanying him is another person with a bunch of switches, and at sight of him the naughty little boys and girls hide. The Christ Child asks that they be forgiven and all promise to be better. Then they are given the gifts and shown the Christmas tree.

Another way of giving presents in France is to wrap them in ever so many papers and boxes and mark them with the child's name, then suddenly throw them into the room.

France has no Santa Claus. His place is taken by Pére Noel. In general he resembles our American Santa Claus but is less jovial and a bit more religious and solemn.

The Christmas tree was not known in France until 1840, when the German Princess of Mecklenburg introduced it into her holiday celebration.

In Brittany there is a pious saying that Christmas night is so holy that the sufferings of those in purgatory cease for a time and a wave of happiness comes over the whole world. No animal sleeps except the serpent.

GERMANY

Tree

Germany is the home of the Christmas tree. There is no home without a tree and twinkling candles and gifts on Christmas Eve.

Some families even have two trees at Christmas, one for the children and one for the grown folks.

"Christ Kind'l"

In Germany instead of Santa Claus the Christ Child (*das Christ Kindlein* or *Christ Kind'l*) is the popular source of Christmas gifts. He is often represented as a sort of combination angel and fairy, impersonated by a girl dressed in white. He appears on Christmas Eve and inquires how the children have behaved, asks them to recite a prayer and sing a hymn, etc., and then distributes the gifts. *Kris Kringle* is a variation of *Christ Kind'l*.

Santa Claus's helpers are the godfathers of the children. All German children visit their godfather's house and there find a gift waiting for them.

"Knecht Ruprecht"

In northern Germany gifts are attributed to *Knecht Ruprecht*. He is represented as a bearded old man covered with fur or straw. His name varies in different localities and in some places he is known as "The Holy Christ."

Blazing Wheel

In one part of Germany people bind a great wheel with straw and take it to the top of a hill near a river. Here they set fire to the straw and start it blazing down the hill. If the straw burns and the wheel rolls into the river, it is a good omen that Santa will come.

Water

An old legend in Germany relates that all water turns to wine at midnight on Christmas Eve, and whoever tries to say "All water turns to wine" will be frightened and punished by the appearance of the devil who will say, "And thou my child art mine." According to another old legend, water drawn from a well or spring at midnight on Christmas Eve will remain fresh throughout the year.

Bells

A German legend tells that on Christmas Eve all the bells of churches, chapels, monasteries, and cities destroyed by war will ring, and whoever listens properly can hear them chime.

Spinning

In North Germany, where the spinning wheel still hums in the cottages, a superstition prevails: one must not spin during the twelve nights after Christmas lest he or she walk after death. Out of the Christmas season, if the spinning is done after sunset on Saturday, it is said that mice will eat the work.

"Lebkuchen" and "Pfeffernuesse" ✖

Kuchen and cakes play an important part in the Christmas celebrations of Germany, there being but few homes where they are not made. Two of the most widely known and most popular are *Lebkuchen* and *Pfeffernuesse*.

Putz ✖ ✖

Many children of German birth living in the United States enjoy their "Putz," which is an elaborate display of toy villages and miniature lanscapes sometimes occupying several rooms. Often animal-shaped cookies are used in the array.

GREECE

Luck of Christ ✖ ✖

Dating back to Byzantine times, it is the custom of children in the Greek Empire to go around on Christmas morning and collect walnuts, figs, raisins, and sweets. This is known as "Luck of Christ."

The Greeks still call their Christmas, "Feast of Lights."

HOLLAND

A quaint and impressive ceremonial is observed in Holland on Christmas Eve. The men of the towns and villages, dressed in various costumes, gather in the public squares. A leader is selected and he carries a large illuminated star mounted upon a pole and following this star, as the Wise Men were guided to Bethlehem, a procession winds through the streets while the *Gloria in Excelsis* is sung. After the parade a supper is served.

A greeting to St. Nicholas is sung by the children:

> Welcome friend; St. Nicholas welcome,
>   Bring no rod for us tonight!
> While our voices bid thee welcome,
>   Every heart with joy is light.

As soon as they have finished singing, the door is opened and in he comes. After asking questions, he pours a shower of candy on the floor and the children scramble for it. When they look up he is gone. Then they leave their wooden shoes on the table or in front of the fireplace and go to bed. Next morning they find the shoes filled with gifts from St. Nicholas.

ICELAND

In Iceland there are only four hours of daylight on Christmas Day, and these are spent in church services.

AMERICAN INDIAN

The American Indians have a superstition that deer kneel and look up to the Great Spirit on Christmas Eve.

IRELAND

Lights in Windows

> On Christmas Eve a Candlelight
> To shine abroad through Christmas night,
> That those who pass may see its glow,
> And walk with Christ a mile or so.

The placing of lights in windows has become very popular in our holiday festivities. It originated from an

Irish custom connected with Christmas. The Irish place lighted candles in their windows on Christmas Eve as a guide and an invitation to all who, like Mary and Joseph on the first Christmas Eve, may be wandering about unable to find quarters for the night. In Ireland poor wanderers and tramps are welcomed everywhere. They are given a good meal, a place to sleep, and are sent on their way in the morning with a bit of money in their pockets.

Another Irish custom connected with Christmas is "Feeding the Wren." The young people of a village get together on St. Stephen's Day (Dec. 26), obtain a wren, place it in a cage, perch the cage on the top of a bush, and go from door to door collecting money for the relief of the supposedly starving wren. The sum of money thus gathered is used to defray the expense of a dance on New Year's.

These lines are recited from door to door while asking for money.

> The wren, the wren, the "King"* of all birds,
> St. Stephen's Day, she caught in the furze,
> Although she is little, her family is great,
> Cheer up land lady and give us a trate [treat].
> We followed this wren, three miles or more,
> We followed this wren, through frost and snow,
> Through hedges and ditches, we tore our breeches,
> From bush to bush and tree to tree
> In Carick-conlish we broke his knee,
> And we brought him home on a holly tree,
> Up with the kettle and down with the pan,
> Give us some silver and let us be gone.

*There was at one time in the spring of the year a great migration of the birds of Ireland and there was an argument between them, that one section of the birds could fly higher than the other. The

"Befana"

In Italy the giving of gifts is advanced to Epiphany as the favored time. Here *Befana,* a corruption of Epiphania, is the benefactress. The same legends are told of her as of the Russian *Babuska* (see Russia), but *Befana* seems also something of a bogy: "Look out or Befana will get you," is a threat for Italian children. The celebration of Epiphany is observed in Italy by a sort of open-air carnival or fair, at which all sorts of booths are set up and toys and sweetmeats of every sort are sold.

In Italy the *Presepio* or crib is as characteristic of

---

eagle said he could fly higher, the skylark said, "No, I can fly higher than you can," and with that they took to flight. The little wren got on the back of the eagle and went up with him. He, never noticing the wren, kept going up while the skylark was flying along beside him. Finally the skylark got tired out and could go no higher. Then the eagle being also tired and, as he thought, the uppermost, started to come down. The little wren flew off his back as he started down and went up higher than all of them, and when he came to earth he was proclaimed the "king" of all birds. He is the smallest one that was at that meeting and raises the largest family of all. He generally raises 18 little ones. His nest is made on the side of a ditch in a mossy bank. It is all of moss and perfectly globular, with an opening in the side about two thirds up the height of the ball that protects him from the wind and rain. He is able to fly only a little way at a time, about three, or four rods, then he takes cover in the long grass and blackberry bushes and when found and scared out, he will go a little farther and take cover again. In that way the boys who are hunting him, finally catch him when he gets tired out. They fasten him on the topmost bough of a holly tree and bring him back in triumph. They sing their song from house to house in their neighborhood. Sometimes they meet another crowd of boys who are on the same business and they have a struggle as to who will have all the money.

Christmas as is the tree in Germany. Every home, even the poorest, has its *Presepio* of some kind and the churches have very elaborate ones. To these the people bring humble gifts of nuts or apples which they place in the hands of the life-sized figures.)

Yule Log

On Christmas Eve the children are blindfolded and gathered round the Yule log reciting verses to the Christ Child. When the log is lighted the blindfolds are removed, and the children find before them gifts which they are told the Christ Child brought.

Church of Ara Coeli, Rome

According to an ancient legend the Emperor Augustus Cæsar asked the sibyl Tiburtina to inquire whether he should consent to allow himself to be worshiped with divine honors which the Senate had decreed upon him. After some days the sibyl took him to an altar, and above the altar in the opening heavens in a glory of light he beheld a beautiful Virgin holding an Infant in her arms while a voice was heard saying, "This is the altar of the Son of the living God." On this same spot in later years a church called *Ara Coeli* was built.

A famous crib is erected every Christmas at this church and children of tender years recite poems or little sermons on a platform in front of it. The infant preachers, whose ages range from four to ten years, go through their task emphasizing their words with graceful gestures.

LABRADOR

Christmas services are held in the churches in Labrador, and for the children the happiest part comes when they are given little lighted candles standing in a turnip which has been specially saved from the harvest for this use. In former years the candles were made of deer tallow, which the children could eat as well as the turnips, but now imported candles are used, and they are not fit to eat, so the children have only the pleasure of seeing them burn.

LITHUANIA

In Lithuania on Christmas Eve a layer of hay is placed on the table under the cloth in memory of the night in Bethlehem, and an unconsecrated wafer symbolizing the love and harmony of the season is shared by all present.

MEXICO

The nine-day Christmas festival dear to the Mexicans is the *Posada*, which means inn. In their homes, the children form in groups and march up stairs and down singing hymns. All doors are shut and the singers knock at each in turn, for they represent the journey of Mary and Joseph to Bethlehem. Each room is supposed to be an inn, and as they knock, someone from inside shouts, "No room at this inn: You cannot enter." When the little pilgrims are tired out, some unexpected door is finally opened and they behold upon a table a doll, representing the Infant Jesus, around which are arranged Christmas greens and toys.

Another quaint and picturesque custom, and one entirely peculiar to Mexico, is the *piñata*. A *piñata* is really nothing more than a dummy, made by the natives and sold, the price varying according to the adornments. The basework is an earthen pot (*olla*) which is filled with candies, nuts, fruits, and numerous other things, not unlike the collection that American children find in the stockings on Christmas morning. The *olla* is ingeniously hidden and no one would guess its existence. Some *piñatas* represent clowns, others ballet dancers, etc., very gorgeously decorated with tissue-paper flowers and streamers. To the head is attached a cord by which it is fastened to the ceiling. When all is prepared, the signal is given and old as well as young join hands and circle around the *piñata,* singing their Christmas carols. Finally one of the party is blindfolded, given a stick and placed in the center of the ring. Being turned round three times, he is told to strike carefully and *con mucha fuerza* (with much force). Nearly always the stroke is made in the wrong direction and laughter and more singing follow. One after another is blindfolded, and has his turn at breaking the *piñata.* Amid applause and yells the poor clown finally collapses and down pours a rain of oranges, candy, and gifts. Then the scramble begins, and each one keeps whatever he manages to get.

MORAVIANS

The church service of the Moravians is devoted to music, and while the choir sings, cake and coffee are served to all the members of the congregation. The children also receive little candles representing the coming of the "Light of the World."

NEW ENGLAND

One thing the Pilgrim Fathers and Puritans did not bring with them was Christmas. They considered the feast a pagan festival, and consequently for many years there was no Christmas in New England. So strict were they in colonial times that in Massachusetts there was a law specifically forbidding anyone to celebrate Christmas. Even today many New England towns make more of Thanksgiving Day than of Christmas. In New Hampshire one big tree often does for the whole town. The tree is set up in the town hall and on it the parents hang up the presents for their children who come there and get them when a short entertainment is given. Decorations are omitted, and when the presents are removed, the tree is perfectly bare.

NEWFOUNDLAND

During Christmas week it is the custom of the fishermen in Newfoundland "to fish for the church," that is, bringing their catch to be sold for the curate of the local parish, and along with this it is quite the custom for all the villagers in outport towns to "chip in" and present him with a great load of wood.

PHILIPPINES

Christmas is a religious festival to the native Filipino and is ushered in early in the morning by the ringing of bells for hours. After the church services, there is a floral procession of the children who sing carols and parade through the streets led by a band.

The Spanish people call the Holy Child *Santo Nino*. There is a very famous image in the Cathedral of the City of Cebu, Philippine Islands. When settlers arrived at Cebu, after the landing of Magellan in 1521, they found the natives were worshiping this doll which they claimed had been mysteriously given to them. It was of European workmanship and it is believed Magellan had left it. It was carefully preserved in the church built by the Augustinian friars and is deeply venerated by the natives.

POLAND

Christmas plays and pageants are popular in Poland. The Christmas story is acted by marionettes while it is told in verse. The boys in costumes go from house to house carrying Christmas cribs and singing carols. It is a Polish custom not to serve the Christmas dinner until the evening star is seen. At the table there is always a vacant chair which, they say, is for the Little Child of Bethlehem.

During the octave of the Epiphany, homes are blessed and the doors marked with the initials of the Wise Men, with chalk blessed on the Feast of the Epiphany.

Before Christmas, wafers are blessed and distributed in the church services. Each member of the family breaks his wafer with each of the other members, the head of the family breaking with the oldest child, and so on. During the breaking they exchange good wishes. The wafers are sent to absent members of their family and friends, not forgetting those in America.

PUERTO RICO

In Puerto Rico the children put boxes on the roofs instead of hanging stockings inside, for Santa to put their gifts in. A most picturesque and beautiful celebration known as "Bethlehem Day" is observed by the children on January 12, in memory of the coming of the Magi. It consists of a procession through the streets led by three children, dressed as the Wise Men of the East in colorful costumes and riding on ponies or horses, holding the gifts for the Infant King in their hands. Then follow numerous angels, shepherds, and flute players.

ROUMANIA

The people of Roumania have a Christmas custom called "Blessing the Danube." Clad in gay costumes to represent Pontius Pilate, Herod, and other Biblical characters, they gather at the river bank and sing carols. After breaking the ice, a wooden cross is thrown into the water and great is the scramble after it, as the one who rescues it is believed to have extraordinary good fortune in store. A special kind of cake called *Turte* is found in every household on Christmas Day. It consists of layers of thin dough and honey or melted sugar, and walnuts and sometimes hemp seed are used. It is prepared the day before, and the custom prevails for the housewife while kneading the dough to go out into the yard followed by her husband with an ax. As they come to a tree, he pretends to threaten to cut it down, arguing that the tree is no good as it does not bear fruit. The wife defends the tree saying she thinks it will be as full of fruit next year as her fingers are full of dough. They pass from tree to tree in this manner until all are visited, but none cut down. The dough is supposed to represent the swaddling clothes of the Infant Christ.

Boys go from house to house and carry a bag for any gifts that they may receive. The object of their visit is to extend Christmas greetings called *Colinde* which consist in reciting verses, and legendary and fanciful stories.

RUSSIA

Babuska (grandmother) is the dispenser of gifts at Christmas time in Russia. The legend goes that once upon a time she refused an opportunity to accompany the Three Kings on their journey and misdirected them, when they inquired their way to Bethlehem. According to another legend, she refused to take the Holy Family in when they were fleeing to Egypt. Regretting this, she goes about on Christmas Eve looking for the Christ Child and distributing gifts to all the children.

In modern Russia, Christmas observance is, of course, against the law. Russian stores are prohibited from selling Christmas toys and from displaying yuletide articles in show windows, and persons cutting Christmas trees or selling them are prosecuted. Artists and singers are forbidden to take part in Christmas programs. St. Nicholas is the Patron Saint of Russia.

SCANDINAVIA

Burning the Yule Log

The burning of the Yule Log was a custom of the Scandinavians during their festival of the winter solstice or turning of the year which they called Yule. The charred ashes were supposed to have magic power.

Sheaf of Grain

A sheaf of grain attached to a long pole is placed outside in the snow-covered yards as a Christmas feast for birds in Scandinavia. Not a peasant will sit down to a meal on Christmas until he has hung a sheaf of corn or wheat outside for the birds. Sometimes suet is tied to trees as an extra feast for birds on Christmas.

"Julanissen"

On Christmas a feast is prepared and left for *Julanissen,* a tiny gnomelike creature who, according to folklore, lives in the household invisibly. It is believed he comes forth to eat when all the household are asleep.

Wheels

The Norwegians let all implements with wheels, as wagons, spinning wheels, etc., rest during the Christmas season. To keep a wheel moving during this time was a great sin against the sun, as it might indicate that they wanted the sun wheel to move faster.

Salt

It was an ancient custom in Norway to feed cattle salt in a cowbell on Christmas Day. By so doing, the cattle would be sure, during the following summer, to come home from the pastures in the evening of their own accord.

Christmas Preparations

All Christmas preparations must be finished before St. Thomas Day, December 21. All butchering and brewing must be ready and enough wood cut to last over the two weeks' celebration, by that day, or some mishap will befall the household.

Witches

Dry spruce is a favorite wood to burn on Christmas Eve because it sends out so many sparks. These prevent witches, who ride through the air on brooms, from coming down the chimney.

It is said that salt put on the fire will also scare them away.

Christmas Morning and Christmas Eve

In Norway, instead of wishing the others a "Merry

Christmas" the member of the household who wakes first sings a little hymn. Before retiring on Christmas Eve the shoes of all the members of the household are placed in a row as a symbol that all will live peacefully together during the year.

Julklapp

It is the custom to give ladies brooches, earrings, and other jewelry at Christmas. These are concealed in a truss of hay or straw or in a bag of chaff, or wrapped numerous times, and thrust in at the door. The recipient spends much effort in locating the gift, and much fun is caused thereby. This is called Julklapp.

IN THE SOUTH

In the South, firecrackers have been used to celebrate Christmas for many years. Christmas Eve there is much the same as the night before Independence Day in the North. The colored people enjoy the noise which adds to the jollity of the celebration for them. They have huge bonfires in the streets, blow horns and trumpets, and there is a great deal of noise and playing jokes and tricks.

SHAKERS

Christmas is observed by the Shakers by a dinner at which men and women eat at the same table, a fact that makes the day different from any other throughout the year, since at all other times the men and women eat at separate tables. They have a church service at sunset on Christmas Day, after which they march to the community house where the dinner is waiting. The men sit at one side and the women at the other of the same table. One after another they rise and lift the right hand, saying,

"God is Love"; then the meal is eaten in silence. When they have finished eating, they rise and sing while still standing at the table, marking time with their hands and feet until finally their bodies begin to sway from side to side in the peculiar manner that has given this sect its name "Shakers."

SPAIN

For the children of Spain, it is the Wise Men, and especially Balthasar, who bring their Christmas gifts. The children place their shoes in rows at the doors and windows where the Wise Men, repeating their pilgrimage each year, may see them and fill them with toys and good things. None of the Spanish children, neither rich nor poor, have Christmas trees. The Christmas toy is the Child Jesus in the crib, made of painted clay. Instead of hanging up their stockings for gifts, their substitute is the *Nacimiento* — the hiding of shoes and slippers.

It was believed in Spain that at midnight on Christmas Eve the Blessed Lady would visit every home in which an image of the Virgin and Babe was kept and bring a special blessing with her.

A special feature of the Christmas celebration in Seville, Spain, is the dancing of the *Siextas*. Ten dancers and choristers participate in the minuetlike dance done to the accompaniment of hymns. It is among the last of religious dances in Christendom.

SWITZERLAND

The Swiss children set one shoe outside the door for two Saturdays preceding Christmas and find it filled with candy and walnuts if they have been good and deserving of any Christmas presents. Then, on Christmas morning, they find their Christmas tree loaded with presents.

It is a saying among the peasants of this country that if one goes to the chicken coop on Christmas Day and clips the wings of the fowls before midnight, it will safeguard them from beasts of prey.

The Swiss peasants claim that straw tied around the trunks of trees in an orchard, if done on Christmas Eve, with a lantern in hand, will make the trees yield a plentiful crop the coming year.

The Tyrolean peasants enjoy the forecasting of the future on Christmas Eve by sitting on the floor, and with the foot, throw the shoe over the shoulder, and then from the position it assumes, predicting what will happen. If the shoe lands sole down, exceptional good luck is in store; if upside down, things will not fare so well.

SYRIA

Syrian children have no Santa Claus, but they know of a tiny camel that accompanied the Wise Men and which was tired and hungry. On Christmas Eve the children leave bowls of water and grain outside their door for this weary little traveler. In the morning the good children find gifts while the bad child has a black mark on his wrist.

UKRAINA

Ukrainian singers go about the villages carrying a manger and sing their folksongs, telling of the birth of Christ.

PART THREE

Christmas Miscellany

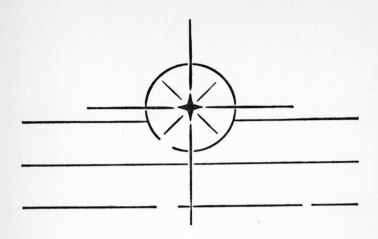

THE CRIB

The First Crib

It was St. Francis of Assisi who gave the Crib or *Presepio,* as it is called in Italy, the tangible form in which we know it today and popularized it. In 1223 he visited Rome and made known to Pope Honorius III his plans of making a scenic representation of the place of the Nativity. The Pope gave his sanction and on Christmas Eve, St. Francis constructed a crib and grouped round it the figures of the Blessed Virgin and St. Joseph, the ass and ox, and the shepherds who came to adore the newborn Saviour. He used live animals in a real stable with a manger to make the scene more vivid to the people.

The custom spread from Italy to Spain, Portugal, France, the Netherlands, and Germany, and from these countries it was spread to all the corners of the earth.

[67]

In the National Museum at Munich, there is a collection of cribs used in Germany, the Tyrol, Italy, and Sicily.

Today in most Catholic churches a crib is found at the Christmas season. Some are masterpieces of the wood carver's art, and others are modeled by the hands of renowned artists; in most cases, however, plaster figures are found. The backgrounds and arrangements are often truly artistic and it is a delightful experience to visit the crib in church on Christmas Day. Some of our museums possess very ancient cribs; in fact, some of the oldest crib figures in existence are found in the United States.

The Metropolitan Museum of Art, New York, has a group which dates from before 1478 (before Columbus discovered America).

Besides those in the churches, little cribs are found in many homes under the Christmas tree. This is a beautiful custom. Apparently the tree has its roots in the crib, sprouting the joys of Christmas from the stable of Bethlehem.

The custom of placing cribs out of doors as Christmas decorations in the yard or rock garden has become popular the past few years. Nothing impresses one more, or is more calculated to instill a true Christmas spirit, than a little crib. Small figures for a crib can be purchased in many stores and are inexpensive. The stable can be made by the children, and no matter how crude when finished, the effect will prove an unlimited source of joy to all.

ST. NICHOLAS (Santa Claus)

St. Nicholas, a bishop of Bari, whose feast is celebrated December 6, is the person we know by the name of Santa Claus. One instance of his generosity is related in the following story: A merchant having lost his fortune, had no dowry to give his three daughters. In those days the lack of a dowry was a serious matter as it doomed a young woman of high birth to a life of extreme poverty and hardship. St. Nicholas, hearing of the plight, threw through an open window of their home, a bag containing money enough to supply the eldest daughter with a dowry. A year later he did the same for the second daughter and the following year he supplied this dowry for the third. The three daughters were thus enabled to marry happily and according to their rank.

Representations of St. Nicholas show him holding a book on which three balls are placed: these three balls represent the three purses. St. Nicholas is the patron of sailors and protector of ships. Men who had much to do with shipping selected him as their patron and the three balls were incorporated into their coat of arms. These men became rich by their trading and in time people went to them to borrow money. Their houses were found by the three balls on their coat of arms. The three golden balls above the pawn shops of our day are a relic of these money lenders of former days.

According to tradition, St. Nicholas died at Myra in Asia Minor on December 5, in the year 345. Here he was buried. In 1087 his body was stolen by some Italian merchants and taken to Bari, Italy, on board a ship. On the journey some sailors hoping to gain a particular blessing, stole some small bones from the casket. At once a terrible storm arose, which did not subside until the bones were again restored to their place. Over his tomb now, there stands a beautiful basilica. A liquid known as *La Manna di san Nicola* flows from his tomb and many miracles have been performed through its use. Strange to say, the children of Italy are not visited by St. Nicholas at the Christmas season, as in other lands.

Where St. Nicholas is the dispenser of gifts he is supposed to make a tour on the eve of his feast day, dressed in his episcopal robes as a bishop with a staff and miter and traveling on a white horse. The object of this tour is to find out how the children have been behaving. When he has gone, the little folks prepare receptacles for expected presents. Shoes, stockings, baskets, boxes, and the like, are placed or hung in conspicuous places, and water and hay are prepared for St. Nicholas's horse. In the morning the children eagerly look for the expected gifts. If they have been good boys and girls, gifts are left and the horse's food is gone, but bad children find switches instead of gifts and the steed's food untouched.

In Europe, St. Nicholas appears under various names and in different guises. He is recognized in such persons as "Holy Man," *Knecht Ruprecht, Niglo, Samiklaus,* "Father Christmas," *Nikolo. Pelznichel* is another variation of St. Nicholas among some Germans. In the New World, he is known as Santa Claus, who is shorn of his episcopal robes and reindeer substituted for the white horse. In some European localities, St. Nicholas does not come alone but acts as an escort for the Christ Child. He never punishes the children. For this purpose he is accompanied by an ugly creature which is known by various names. In Austria he is known as *Krampus*. Sometimes this creature is dressed like the devil and is called *Klaubauf, Putenmandel,* or *Buzemann.* Santa Claus in our country has been bereft of his religious significance and remains but a myth.

LEGENDS ABOUT ST. NICHOLAS

St. Nicholas and the Grain

During a grievous famine, St. Nicholas learned there were vessels in port laden with corn. He desired the captains to supply him with a portion for the people. They replied that they dared not, for it was all measured and must be delivered into the Emperor's granaries. St. Nicholas insisted, assuring them that they would suffer no loss. At last, they yielded and found, as he had said, that they had none the less to deliver at Constantinople. The corn, moreover, that St. Nicholas gave to the people increased so miraculously that they had enough for two successive years. During this famine, while traveling, St. Nicholas lodged in the house of an evilly disposed man, who, when other provisions failed, stole and killed little children and salted them for eating. This cruel man offered some of this fearful food to St. Nicholas, who at once perceived the wickedness of the host. Going to the tub which contained the remains, he made the sign of the cross over it, whereupon three children arose, alive and well. These he restored to their mother, a poor widow, and the fame of this wonderful miracle spread far and wide.

St. Nicholas and the Jew

After the death of St. Nicholas, a Jew who could not help believing in his power, set an image of the saint over his treasures to guard them, but notwithstanding this, they were all stolen by robbers. Full of rage the Jew struck the image and mutilated it. That night St. Nicholas appeared to the robbers, wounded and bleeding, to desire them to restore the stolen property. They were so alarmed that they at once obeyed, and the Jew became converted by the miracle.

St. Nicholas and the Miser

As St. Nicholas was distributing gifts one Christmas Eve, he found himself with an empty purse and no food or lodging for the night. He knocked at a door and was admitted, only to find he was in the home of a notorious miser. This man recognized the saint and had heard of his generosity, so thinking he would be richly rewarded, he welcomed him and gave him the best bed in the house. "How did it happen," asked the saint, "that you are rich and your neighbors scarcely keep from starving." "Because I keep my money and help myself," chuckled the old miser. Little more was said, and the saint went to bed. In the morning as St. Nicholas was ready to leave, he told the miser that he had no money to give him, but would bestow his blessing. "Whatever you first start doing this day," said the saint, "you will continue doing until night," and he departed. As the miser was thinking what he could do to make more money, a poor woman came to beg.

His thoughts still on his money, the miser opened his purse and flung a coin to the woman, who thanked him and left. Having started giving away money, he had to continue doing it until nightfall. The news quickly passed and poor people thronged to his house and none left without a coin. It was the best Christmas the people ever had, and from that day, the old man was no longer a miser, which was the blessing bestowed upon him by St. Nicholas.

IS THERE A SANTA CLAUS?

"We take pleasure in answering at once and thus prominently the communication below, expressing at the same time our great gratification that its faithful author is numbered among the friends of *The Sun;*

'Dear Editor — I am eight years old. Some of my little friends say there is no Santa Claus. Papa says, "If you see it in *The Sun,* it's so." Please tell me the truth, is there a Santa Claus?

Virginia O'Hanlon,
115 West Ninety-fifth Street,

"Virginia, your little friends are wrong. They have been affected by the skepticism of a skeptical age. They do not believe except they see. They think that nothing can be which is not comprehensible by their little minds. All minds, Virginia, whether they be men's or children's, are little. In this great universe of ours man is a mere insect, an ant, in his intellect, as compared with the boundless world about him, as measured by the intelligence capable of grasping the whole truth and knowledge. Yes, Virginia, there is a Santa Claus. He exists as certainly as love and generosity and devotion exist, and you know that they abound and give to your life its highest beauty and joy. Alas! how dreary would be the world if there were no Santa Claus! It would be as dreary as if there were no Virginias. There would be no childlike faith then, no poetry, no romance to make tolerable this existence. We should have no enjoyment except in sense and sight. The eternal light with which childhood fills the world would be extinguished. Not believe in Santa Claus! You might as well not believe in fairies! You might get your papa to hire men to watch in all the chimneys on Christmas Eve to catch Santa Claus, but even if they did not see Santa Claus coming down, what would that prove? Nobody sees Santa Claus, but that is no sign that there is no Santa Claus. The most real things in the world are those that neither children nor men can see. Did you ever see fairies dancing on the lawn? Of course not, but that's no proof that they are not there. Nobody can conceive or imagine all the wonders there are unseen and unseeable in the world. You tear apart the baby's rattle to see what makes the noise inside, but there is a veil covering the unseen world which not the strongest man, nor even the united strength of all the strongest men that ever lived, could tear apart. Only faith, fancy, poetry, love, romance, can push aside that curtain and view and picture the supernal beauty and glory beyond. Is it all real? Ah, Virginia, in all this world there is nothing else real and abiding.

"No Santa Claus! Thank God! he lives, and he lives forever. A thousand years from now, Virginia, nay, ten times ten thousand years from now, he will continue to make glad the heart of childhood."*

How Santa Became a Toymaker

A story of interest to children relates how Santa Claus became a toymaker. Hundreds of years ago when Santa was a little boy, he had a crippled sister whom he loved dearly. The little girl, whose name was Santelle, loved her brother dearly, too. He used to go out every day and get pretty stones and flowers for her to play with, and in the evening he told her stories and did all sorts of tricks to make her laugh. But at Christmas time, Santa was a bit sad because their father was too poor to buy Santelle any real toys. Near Christmas time as Santa was just nine years old, he made up his mind that he would get some toys for Santelle. He went to the old toymaker who made toys for the rich children and asked him for some cheap leftover toys for his little crippled sister. The cross old toymaker told Santa that poor children could not have toys. Right then, Santa vowed that when he became a man, he would see to it that all poor children had toys at Christmas time. He returned home and went to work in the cellar of his house, and nobody knew what he was doing although they could hear him hammering and sawing every day.

At last Christmas came and he brought up from the cellar a great big doll house, big enough for Santelle to sit in, and some small toys like jack-in-the-boxes and jumping jacks. Santelle was so delighted that she cried. It was the happiest Christmas the Clauses ever had.

---

*Originally printed September 21, 1897, in *The Sun,* New York. Reprinted with permission.

Right after Christmas, Santa started to make toys so that all the poor children of the town could have some the following Christmas. He made so many and made them so well that after the poor children had theirs, there still were some left which Santa sold to the rich children. After that the rich children never bought any more toys from the cross old toymaker, because Santa's toys were better. Santa has grown older and merrier since then, but he still makes toys to give to the children on Christmas Day.

Santa Claus's Reindeer

One Christmas morning, many, many years ago, the Lord was so pleased with the prayers of the children that He wished to reward them for their love for Him. He asked St. Nicholas if he would take gifts to all the good little children every Christmas. The Lord told him that he could carry the gifts in a sleigh and that he might choose whatever animals he wanted to draw it. St. Nicholas was puzzled and after three days an angel appeared to him and told him to let a child decide for him. So St. Nicholas, with a child, went into the Lord's animal kingdom, where the lion growled, the elephant swung his trunk, and all the animals seemed displeased; all but six lovely little reindeer which laid their heads on the ground and tenderly looked up at the child. "These," said St. Nicholas, "shall be my choice."

Santa and the Chimney

Santa took the idea of coming down the chimney from an old English notion, which was that sweeping down the chimney at New Year's was necessary so that good luck could enter in.

Town of Santa Claus — Indiana

About seventy-five years ago this town applied for a post office and asked Santa Fe as a name, but there already was a post office by that name in Indiana. As it was a short time before Christmas, the people decided to name the town Santaclause, in one word. In 1928, the name was changed to two words, Santa Claus. Since then letters from all over the world have come in, until now it takes a force of about eight people through November and December to handle the Christmas mail with a new electric canceling machine. About 60,000 pieces a day are dispatched around Christmas. This is the only town in the world by that name. A Santa Claus headquarters is maintained where thousands of tourists and visitors buy gifts and post cards. During the Christmas week, Santa Claus in full uniform and long whiskers presides.

St. Wenceslaus, or Wenzel

Some people connect St. Wenceslaus with Christmas giving. There is a familiar legend of St. Wenceslaus, that one cold winter night, when he went out, as his custom was, to carry food and fuel to the poor, his aged servant, who accompanied him, was so overcome by cold that he felt he could go no farther. The saint bade him set his feet in the footprints he made before him, and when the old man did so, warmth came from them and put life into him, so that he could aid St. Wenceslaus in his good works without danger from the cold.

Concerning Santa Claus

As noted, St. Nicholas is vested as a bishop in European countries, which is as it should be. It seems it was right here in America that Santa was given his change of clothes and became a red-faced, bewhiskered gentleman of the jester type.

The idea of the Christ Child bringing the gifts should be emphasized, for after all, He is the real giver, and Christmas is His birthday.

THE CHRISTMAS TREE
CHRISTMAS TREE LEGENDS

The First Christmas Tree

A legend tells that some distance from the home of
the Holy Family in Nazareth, there lived a poor widow
with seven children who were playmates of Jesus. Often-
times Mary would invite these poor children into her
house and give them bread and other things to eat. On
Jesus' seventh birthday His mother gave Him many gifts,
and made things for Him to eat. After a day of happiness,
the little Jesus went to bed thinking of His poor playmates
who certainly never received such presents for their birthday. Little Jesus arose and called seven angels who immediately were at His command. He gathered together an
armful of His presents and, still in His little nightgown,
started out for the home of His playmates at the other
end of town. On the way thither, He sent one angel to get
clothes and shoes and stockings, another to get cakes and
sweets, a third angel He sent for fruits from Paradise,
another was sent to fetch glittering stars from the heavens
above. Each angel was given a duty to perform.

Very soon they all arrived laden with treasures at the

house of the poor widow with seven children. Here it was dark and quiet, as they had long since gone to bed. In the little garden in front of the small house, between the summertime potato patch and flower beds, there stood a single fir tree, still green in the midst of winter and providing a shelter for birds. Little Jesus hung the fine things that He and the angels brought among the branches of the tree. The angels helped Jesus and fastened the especially nice things on the highest branches which He could not reach. Now and then a golden hair from an angel's head would catch in the green needles of the tree and remain hanging to the branches. On each limb and twig there was now dangling some thing or other, a gift, an apple, shoes, nuts which turned a golden color at the angels' touch, toys, little shirts, and even glittering heavenly stars.

After the last gift was hung on the tree, Little Jesus dismissed the angels with many thanks and went to His home as silently as He came, and got back into His little bed as though nothing had happened. You can imagine the joy and happiness at the home of the poor children when they found the little green tree in the snow laden with treasures. They clasped hands and danced around the "Wonder Tree." But far happier was the little boy Jesus. He was so elated that He decided to provide this same happiness each year on His birthday for many others, but especially for children.

The Druids' Tree

When St. Boniface (St. Winfrid) was preaching Christianity to the people of Germany, he found them one Christmas Eve gathered round a huge oak tree to offer a human sacrifice according to the Druid rites of the pagans. In anger St. Boniface bravely hewed down the oak tree, and as it fell there appeared in its place a tall young fir tree. Seeing this, he said to the people, "This new tree is unstained by blood, see how it points to the sky, call it the tree of the Christ Child. Take it up and carry it into the castle of your chief. No longer shall you observe your secret and wicked rites in the shadow of the forest, but you shall hold ceremonies in your own home, that speak of the message of peace and good will to all. A day is coming when there shall not be a home in the land where on the birthday of Christ, the whole family will not gather round the fir tree in memory of this day and to the glory of God." The custom of the Christmas tree has found its place in the remotest corners of the earth since the passing of St. Boniface.

The Robbers

There is a quaint legend that on one cold night in December, many, many years ago, a cry was heard to ring out from the depth of an evergreen forest and two vicious-looking men bearing a heavy sack between them emerged. Sitting down they opened the sack and were amazed to find it filled with toys of all descriptions and sweetmeats. They became very angry and began throwing the things at each other and at the surrounding trees. Soon the trees were filled with dolls, drums, horns, and many other toys which lodged in the branches of the pine trees. When there was nothing more to throw, the robbers grappled with each other and rolled down into a deep ravine. Nothing more was ever heard of them. Meanwhile, an old graybeard, who had been the victim of these robbers, had found help, and with a party of young peasants, returned to the woods where he was robbed, hoping to find his stolen property. As they reached the spot where the robbers had been, a thousand dancing lights appeared and settled on the boughs of the pine trees, which were laden with toys. The peasants were astonished beyond measure and looked at the strange old man, who smiled and said, "You have been kind to Father Christmas, now accept the gifts he offers you. These are yours." He then disappeared.

Origin of the Christmas Tree

According to an ancient legend, when Christ was born, three trees, an olive tree, a date palm, and a pine tree, stood about the manger. To honor the newborn King, the olive gave its fruit and the palm its dates as an offering, but the pine tree had nothing to give.

Some stars, seeing this from above, gently descended from the heavens and rested themselves upon its boughs as an offering. This pleased the Christ Child greatly and was the origin of the first Christmas tree.

*   *   *

Perhaps the use of a tree at Christmas time may be connected with the ancient belief that trees blossom on the night of the Nativity. It may also be connected with a legend of St. Joseph of Arimathea, which tells that when the saint settled at Glastonbury, he planted his staff in the earth and it put forth leaves, blooming on Christmas Eve, ever after that.

That the Christmas tree comes to us from the Germans is the general opinion. A pretty story of its origin is told in Germany. A forester and his family were gathered round the fire on Christmas Eve, when suddenly there was a knocking on the door. The forester, on opening the door, beheld a child, cold and exhausted. The little boy of the family welcomed the child gladly, got him something to eat and gave up his own bed to him. In the morning, the family was awakened by beautiful singing, and looking into the room where the child was, they found Him in a blaze of glory and recognized in Him the Infant Saviour. Before departing, the Heavenly Guest went out, broke off a branch of a fir tree and set it on the ground. "This is My gift to you for your goodness," said He. "This tree shall always be green and bear fruit on Christmas, and you shall always have plenty at that season."

The Shepherd's Twins

Joan and John, two small children and twins, came running across the hillsides of Bethlehem to their father who was watching sheep near by. "Father," they said, "come and see what we have found. We have found two baby trees and they are green, even though it is wintertime." The father sat down and took the children on his knees, telling them they must be fir trees and asked more about them. "Oh," said the children, "the trees are very small and grow very close together as if they loved each other. We will take care of them so that they will grow up with us." The father then sent the children home, telling them he must watch the sheep. Every day after that time, the children visited the twin trees. They were straight, strong little trees, that pointed up to heaven all the time. The children grew to love the trees.

Later, one cold winter night, Joan and John heard their father telling their mother about a wonderful thing that happened. He said that while he and the other shepherds were watching their sheep, angels appeared and told them that the Son of God was born in Bethlehem, and a bright star shone and sent its light straight from heaven to the cave where the Infant Jesus lay. All the shepherds were going down to see Him and bring Him gifts. One had fruit, another had two doves, and the head shepherd had two snow-white lambs from the flock. The twins' father had a piece of lace to give to the Blessed Mother. John and Joan began to cry. "We want to go to see the Holy Babe," they sobbed. "But you have nothing to give Him," said their mother, "and we are too poor to buy a gift." "We will give the trees," they answered. "We love them so much that we know the Baby will love them too," and they ran to the hillside after the little fir trees. They carefully dug them up, root and all, then caught up with the shepherds on their way to the cave in Bethlehem.

In the cave they found the Infant Jesus on a bed of straw. The shepherds and the twins bowed and came close to Him offering their gifts. The Holy Babe turned His eyes to them and then held out His tiny arms to the trees that the twins had brought. The shepherds planted the trees near Jesus, and tied a lamb to each tree, and hung the fruit on the boughs and let the doves rest in the branches, so that the trees were full of gifts. And then the star from heaven shone down on them and lighted them up so brightly that they could be seen a long way off. That is why Christmas trees are filled with gifts and lights. The first ones held gifts for Jesus and lights from a star in heaven.

Why the Christmas Tree Has Tinsel

Of course, every Christmas tree has tinsel on it, and this is how it came about. Many years ago, there lived a good woman who had a large family of children. This woman was immaculately clean about the house and everything she did was spic-and-span. One Christmas Eve she prepared a tree for the children and trimmed it with all sorts of things. During the night spiders visited the tree and crawled from branch to branch leaving their webs behind them. The Christ Child saw this and knew that the good woman, who was so clean about her house, would feel very badly in the morning when she showed the children the tree and found it covered with cobwebs. To reward her for the goodness she did to others, He blessed the Christmas tree and all the spider webs were transformed into silver. In the morning, the good woman showed her children the tree, and lo and behold she herself had never seen such a beautiful tree before. It was all resplendent with threads of silver. That is why we put tinsel on the Christmas tree.

Christmas-Tree Candles

Long, long ago a man was lost in a great woods. For days he wandered through the woods and over the meadows but he always found himself back at the place from which he started. At last when he was so worn out that he thought he must die, night came on. It was one of those beautiful blue nights, and the heavens were filled with bright stars. By the light of the stars, he saw the pathway which he had lost. When he reached his home, he found it was Christmas Eve. It was the light of the Christmas stars which had brought him back to his wife and children, so in thansksgiving he went to the woods again and cut down a small tree and covered it with little lighted candles, which, like the stars in the Christmas sky, burned to honor the birthday of the Christ Child.

TREE EMBLEMS

The Egyptians regarded the date palm as an emblem of immortality and of the starlit firmament and at the time of the winter solstice they decked their homes with its branches. It was held by them to be a symbol of life.

The range of human existence is symbolized by a tree in many of the ancient faiths. It is called "Tree of Life," "World Tree," or "Tree of Existence." The old English Maypole is the same tree bursting into beauty in the spring. In the early calendars, Adam and Eve were commemorated on Christmas Eve, their symbol being the tree of the knowledge of good and evil. The next day was the day of Christ whose symbol was the tree of life or the cross. So the tree became associated with the Nativity.

SERVICE TREE

A Scandinavian myth speaks of a "Service Tree" sprung from the blood-drenched soil where two lovers had been killed by violence. During the Christmas season mysterious lights, which no wind could extinguish, were often seen glowing in its branches.

CHRISTMAS-TREE TRIMMING

Have a Christmas tree and be sure *you* trim one yourself, if not for yourself, for someone else. There are always plenty of people for whom to trim a Christmas tree; perhaps some poor people you know or some very old person living alone who is sure not to have a Christmas tree. You may imagine how happy such persons would be if on Christmas Eve someone knocked at their door and going there, they saw no one at all but a Christmas tree all trimmed. Ornaments, tinsel, and lights are sold so reasonably in the stores, that the cost of a tree is nothing compared with the happiness it gives to both the giver and receiver. If the tree is for elderly persons, they will enjoy it more if some of the trimmings are homemade and old-fashioned. Popcorn is easily strung, and by making a chain of six kernels, then adding two cranberries, and repeating this arrangement, a pretty effect is obtained. Popcorn balls, wrapped in wax paper, may contain a surprise in the center. A coin or small gift concealed in this way will produce a laugh when found. Peanuts and walnuts can be gilded or wrapped in tin foil and hung separately or in clusters. A walnut with the meat removed and a fortune written on paper substituted, and the halves of the shell pasted together again, and then hung on the tree, will bring a chuckle when opened. Pieces of straw cut and strung with raisins and cranberries make novel if old-fashioned trimmings. Little cornucopias made of gilt and silver paper with a picture pasted on the outside are especially pretty. A few cookies cut in odd shapes, stars, crescents, animals, etc., and an apple or two should not be forgotten. Finally, make it a point that there is a silver star fastened to the top of the tree if possible. If such a tree is trimmed for some poor, old person, it is not difficult to imagine what memories it recalls and the happiness it renews. Try this just once, and after that Christmas will hardly seem Christmas if you have not helped trim a tree.

HOLLY — MISTLETOE — POINSETTIA

Holly

It is believed that it was from a holly bush that God spoke to Moses in the wilderness. One legend tells us that, because the holly kept secret the whereabouts of our Saviour when His enemies were searching for Him, it was rewarded the privilege of keeping its green leaves all winter. People who are superstitious believe that holly planted near a dwelling will protect the house from lightning. Holly is called Christ-thorn in Denmark. An old legend relates that on the first Christmas night, when the shepherds went to the cave, a little lamb following the shepherds was caught by the holly thorn and the red berries are the blood drops which froze on the branches.

There are more than 150 varieties of holly and it grows in practically all countries of the world. It was used at the Christmas winter festivals and in ancient times as a symbol of immortality, because it bore fruit in the winter season.

According to an ancient belief, holly berries possess and give wonderful power when worn in the shape of a wreath. It was thought if the wearer went alone at midnight on Christmas and sat in a church in the dark, second sight would come to him and into the church would file those of his friends who were to die during the coming year. In some parts of England, it is believed that unless every bit of holly is removed from the house by Twelfth-night some ill luck will happen.*

Mistletoe

The mistletoe was a plant sacred to the Druid priests of old England. They cut it from the boughs where it grew, with a golden sickle never used for any other purpose. These twigs were then given to young men who carried them to the homes of the people, whose duty it was to accept them and show appreciation by giving the priest gifts. The mistletoe was then hung over their doors and it was thought only happiness could pass under the branch. That is said to be the origin of the mistletoe-kiss tradi-

---

*Removal of Christmas decorations from the houses and churches is often reserved for the twelfth day after Christmas, or Epiphany.

tion, which holds that any man may kiss the girl he catches under the mistletoe. The mistletoe was also supposed to have healing powers, although none are found by modern science.

According to mythology, the Sun God Balder was slain by an arrow made of mistletoe. Every plant in the world had sworn not to harm him except the mistletoe which on account of its feebleness had not been asked. Loki, jealous of Balder, made an arrow from the despised plant and placed it in the hands of the blind god Hoder, who unknowingly hurled the shaft which brought death to the Sun God.

The Church regards the mistletoe as an entirely pagan symbol and refuses to allow it to participate with the holly and evergreen in the Christmas decorations. There is an ancient belief that the mistletoe was the tree from which the holy cross was hewn and that after this was made the plant withered.

Poinsettia

The poinsettia has no Christmas tradition. Possessing the beautiful red and green leaves (the flowers themselves being the small yellow centers), and being available at this season, their brilliance adds extensively to Christmas decorations. This plant is native to Central America and Mexico and was adapted some years ago to cultivation by Dr. Poinsett of Charleston, South Carolina. It is distinctly modern and American.

VARIOUS REGARDING CHRISTMAS
THE DATE OF CHRISTMAS

The Year in Which Christ Was Born

The exact year of the nativity cannot be proved, but critics generally accept 4 B.C. as the probable year. Herod died 714 years after the founding of Rome, which is 4 B.C., as we know it. Herod was dead before the passover, which took place April 12, 4 B.C.

The First Christmas Observance

Tradition says that Christmas was first celebrated in A.D. 98. It was ordered to be held as a solemn feast by Pope Telesphorus in A.D. 137. There is no record of any commemoration of the day during the life of Christ.

December 25 Fixed as Christmas

About A.D. 340, St. Cyril made careful investigation as to the date of Christ's birth and reported December 25 as the most probably correct date. Pope Julius accepted this and established the festival at Rome on this date, which was accepted by every nation in Christendom.

Origin of the Custom

The custom of giving presents was a feature of the Romans during their winter festival, the Saturnalia. The early Christians made presents to their children on Christmas morning, under the pretense that they were the gift of the Christ Child. There is no country in the civilized world that has not in some form or another the custom of giving presents either at Christmas or around the Christmas season, and this age-old custom can be traced to the dawn of history.

Boxing Day

Old English Christmas-giving came to have a peculiar manifestation known as "boxing." Servants, apprentices, etc., used to go around at Christmas with earthen boxes to collect their Christmas presents in the form of money. Consequently, another name for Christmas Day was "Boxing Day." Some would reject the explanation of the term "boxing" and derive it from the Arabic Backsheesh — tip, gratuity.

Man in the Moon

A pretty German legend in connection with Christmas giving is the following: One Christmas Eve, long, long ago, a peasant set out to steal some cabbages from a neighbor's garden. As he filled his basket, the Christ Child appeared on a white horse and said to him: "Because thou hast stolen on the holy night instead of giving, thou shalt sit in the moon with thy basket of cabbage," which the peasant did immediately and is doing to this day.

Christmas Carols

The practice of singing Christmas carols appears to be almost as old as the celebration of the day itself. In the first days of the Church, the bishops sang carols on Christmas Day. They recall the songs sung by the angel at the birth of Christ.

Christmas Waits

The word *waits,* probably meaning *watchers,* is restricted to the singers of carols on Christmas morning. In Italy, bagpipers dressed as shepherds, go from house to house, singing the shepherd song *Cantata dei pastori.*

THE STAR OF BETHLEHEM

Biblical authorities claim that the supernatural appearance of light in the heavens at the time of Christ's birth was not a real star in the ordinary sense of the word. According to an ancient commentary on St. Matthew, the star on its first appearance had the form of a radiant child bearing a scepter or cross.

ADVENT

The four weeks of Advent preceding Christmas represent the four great prophesies concerning the coming of the Saviour in the Old Testament. The first promise of the Redeemed was made in Paradise after the fall of our first parents: the woman and her Son would crush the head of the serpent. The second promise is found in the story of Abraham. This patriarch was chosen as the father of a new nation, and in his seed all the nations of the earth would be blessed. Out of the nation of Abraham the family of David was selected, and out of this family

[92]

the Saviour of the world would be born, fulfilling the third promise. Finally, out of David's family a person was to spring forth, the Virgin Mother of Christ. "A Virgin will bring forth a Son and His name shall be called Emmanuel, God with us."

THREE MASSES

Every Roman Catholic priest is accorded the right to celebrate three Masses on Christmas Day, first at midnight, another at dawn, and the third in the full light of the day. They are known as Christ Mass, Angel Mass, and High Mass. The first Mass is celebrated in memory of the birth of our Saviour, according to the flesh; the second Mass is offered to honor the birth of Jesus, Son of God and of the Virgin Mary; the third Mass commemorates the eternal birth of the Son in the bosom of the Father.

"MERRIE CHRISTMAS"

The old Saxon word *Merrie,* did not mean gay and lively as our English word, but it meant pleasant and agreeable. It is typical of England.

VARIOUS NAMES FOR CHRISTMAS

The French call the holiday *Noël* or *Nowel.* The Scotch use the name *Yule,* and the Scandinavians *Juletide.* The Welsh call Christmas *Nadolig,* and the Italians call it *Il Natale,* while the Germans call it *Weihnachten.* In Polish the term *Boze Narodzenie,* is used, meaning "God's Nativity." The Bohemians and Croatians say *Bozic,* and the Slovaks, *Vianoce.* In Spanish, the word *Navidad,* meaning "Nativity," is used.

"Xmas"

X is an abbreviation for Christ. It originated from the Greek letter X (ch) beginning the name of Christ (the anointed).

CHRISTMAS FLAG

Though centuries old in its use, the "Banner of the Cross" is new to most of us as a part of Christmas celebrations. The colors of the Christmas flag are red and green. Within a ground of red is a ground of green and within the green is a red cross.

Use of Red at Christmas

White is the Christmas color of the Roman Catholic and Anglican churches. Red, as applied, has no religious significance; it is used solely because of its brilliancy.

OLD CHRISTMAS SAYINGS

Christmas proverbs are interesting and numerous. Each people has its own collection. They are, however, without any significance except for the grain of truth they sometimes contain. They very frequently contradict one another, as will be seen in the following:

> So now is come our joy full'st feast;
> Let every man be jolly;
> Each room with ivy leaves is drest,
> And every post with holly.
> — *George Wither*

Christmas comes but once a year, and when it comes it brings good cheer.

Bounce buckram, velvet's dear,
Christmas comes but once a year;
And when it comes, it brings good cheer;
But when it's gone, it's never near.

For Christmas comes but once a year,
And then they shall be merry.
— *George Wither*

Irish Version:

For Christmas comes but wanst a year
And when it come it brings good cheer,
And when it goes it laves us here
And what'll we do for the rest o' the year?

After Christmas comes Lent.

Now's now, but Yule's in winter.

A white Easter bringeth a green Christmas.

A warm Christmas, a cold Easter; a green Christmas, a white Easter.

A light Christmas a heavy sheaf

or

A dark Christmas makes a heavy wheat-sheaf.

A green Christmas is neither handsome nor healthful.

A black Christmas maketh a fat churchyard.

Easter in snow, Christmas in mud;
Christmas in snow, Easter in mud.

If at Christmas ice hangs on the willow, clover may be cut at Easter.

If ice will bear a man before Christmas, it will not bear a goose after.

[95]

If St. Michael brings many acorns,
Christmas will cover the fields with snow.

Whitesuntide wet,
Christmas fat.

He hath eaten many a Christmas pie.

A Yule feast may be quit at Pasch (Easter).

They keep Christmas all the year.

Another year will bring another Christmas.

A child that's born on Christmas Day,
Is fair and wise, and good and gay.

A kiss at Christmas and an egg at Easter.

At Christmas great loafs, at Easter clean souls, at Whitsuntide
new clothes.

It smells of Muscadel like an English Christmas.

St. Andrew, the king, three weeks and three days before Christmas comes in.

At Christmas time or a little after, a crab in the hedge and
thanks to the grafter.

The devil makes his Christmas pie of lewd tongues.

The devil makes his Christmas pies of clerk's fingers and lawyers'
tongues.

> If Christmas Day on a Sunday fall
> A troublous winter we shall have all.
> If Christmas on a Monday be,
> Then a great winter we shall see.

Ghosts never appear on Christmas Eve.

Yule is come, and Yule is gone,
And we have feasted well,
So Jack must to his flail again,
And Jenny to her wheel.

Long-winded schismatics shall rule the roast,
And Father Christmas mourn his revels lost.
— *Swift*

Life still hath one romance that naught can bury —
Not Time himself, who coffins Life's romances —
For still will Christmas gild the year's mischances,
If Childhood comes, as here, to make him merry.
— *Theodore Watts-Dunton*

THE FIRST CHRISTMAS CARDS

The first real Christmas cards appear to have been printed in London in 1846. Almost one thousand copies were printed, and that was considered a very large sale. It was not until about 1860 that the custom of using cards to convey Christmas greetings became popular, and has gained in strength ever since, until now Christmas cards are produced by the millions. Cards with pictures of the Nativity, the Madonnas, Wise Men and Camels, or Shepherds are ideal and should be preferred. They convey a finer spiritual feeling than pictures of Santa Claus, holly, poinsettias, ships, etc.

CHRISTMAS A LEGAL HOLIDAY

Christmas is a legal holiday in all the states of the United States and derives its sanction from the state, not from national authority.

THE CHRISTMAS SUN

The sun is thought to leap twice in its joy and change its course on Christmas Day.

QUARRELS

There is an old saying that if you quarrel or are cross on Christmas Day, things will go wrong the whole coming year.

CHRISTMAS FOODS

Plum Pudding and Mince Pie

These were originally called Christmas pudding and Christmas pie. The mixture of spices are emblematical of the offerings brought to the Infant Christ by the Wise Men. The "Christmas pie" was formerly made in the shape of a cradle emblematical of the manger in which Jesus was laid. To represent the manger, strips of pastry were sometimes laid crosswise over the pie. Both date back to the early days of the Christians and were considered a test of orthodoxy, as some of the ingredients were held in abomination by the Jews.

Cookies

It is said that Christmas cookies are a survival of the giving of confections to the Roman Senators during the festivities of Christmas time in the early ages.

"PSALMS"

Some people say that to find out how many years you will live, you must take a Bible on Christmas and the first psalm to strike your eye contains in stanzas the number of years granted you to live.

ONION

An age-old Christmas Eve custom, believed in by many and repeated annually, is to take a perfect specimen of onion and cut it into halves. Peel off twelve layers (one for each month of the year to come), and fill each with salt. On the following morning the peelings which contain damp salt indicate rainy months, while the peelings with dry salt, will be fair months.

THE CHRISTMAS SEAL

It was in 1904 that the Christmas seal originated in Copenhagen, Denmark. A children's hospital was needed in that city and Einar Holboell, a postal clerk, conceived the idea that stamps especially designed to decorate Christmas letters and packages would and could be made to finance the cost of the building. The idea was endorsed by the Danish royal family and the first Christmas seal was designed and placed on sale in the post office of that country. The citizens of Denmark purchased enough to insure medical care for the sick children. Jacob Riis, in America, who was interested in social service, received a letter from his mother country bearing one of the bright stamps and inquired about its purpose. The possibilities of its use in the United States impressed him and he wrote an article describing what the stamp had achieved in Denmark, which article was published in the *Outlook*. Inspired by that article, Miss Emily O. Bissell, of Wilmington, Delaware, organized the first sale of Christmas seals in the United States and as a result a $3,000 tuberculosis pavilion was built. In 1908, Miss Bissell induced the American Red Cross authorities to undertake a nation-wide sale of Christmas stamps, and from then until

[99]

1920, the Red Cross conducted the sale of seals. The National Tuberculosis Association had been organizing from 1907 to 1910, with little funds. To strengthen the organization the American Red Cross joined with it in the sale of Christmas seals. This partnership lasted until 1920 when it was dissolved and since then only the double-barred cross emblem of the antituberculosis movement has appeared on Christmas seals.

PLACES NAMED CHRISTMAS

Christmas Island

Christmas Island, in the Pacific Ocean, is so named because Captain Cook landed there Christmas Day, 1777.

Towns Named Christmas

Five communities in the United States are named for the Yule holiday. There is a Christmas in Gila County, Arizona; Orange County, Florida; Lawrence County, Kentucky; Bolivar County, Mississippi; and Roane County, Tennessee.

Minnesota, the "Land of Lakes" boasts of a lake by the name of Christmas. It is located in Scott County.

LIGHTS IN WINDOWS

Many people believe that the Christ Child wanders over the world on Christmas Eve and set lights in the windows of their home to guide Him.

CHRISTMAS FLOWERS

A story is told that a poor man, coming home from work one Christmas Eve, found a little lost child. He was cold and crying. Pitying him, the poor man carried him to his home where he showed his wife and family what he had found. They welcomed the child and gave him of their scanty meal, after which the children played with him like a brother. As they were ready to go to bed, the little stranger grew tall and a halo appeared round his head. "Bless us," said the mother, "it is the Lord Himself." Immediately the vision vanished. Next morning they looked for some trace of the stranger and when they arrived at the place where the child was first seen, the ground was covered with flowers.

Blue Flower

There is a story that on Christmas Eve a flower that will cure any kind of sickness falls from heaven. It is called "Blue Flower" and can be found only by the pure of heart.

B.C. AND A.D.

One of the most potent, though silent testimonials of the Divinity of Christ, is the indisputable fact that all chronology is dated "before" or "after" Christ. B.C. and A.D. meet and part at His crib. It is no mere accident, but a fact that can be explained in only one way.

PART FOUR

Christmas Carols and Poems

SELECTED LIST OF CHRISTMAS POEMS

A CHRISTMAS CHANT

Gloria in excelsis!
Sound the thrilling song;
In excelsis Deo!
Roll the hymn along.
Gloria in excelsis!
Let the heavens ring;
In excelsis Deo!
Welcome, new-born King.
Gloria in excelsis!
Over the sea and land,
In excelsis Deo!
Chant the anthem grand,
Gloria in excelsis!
Let us all rejoice;
In excelsis Deo!
Lift each heart and voice.
Gloria in excelsis!
Swell the hymn on high;
In excelsis Deo!
Sound it to the sky.
Gloria in excelsis!
Sing it, sinful earth,
In excelsis Deo!
For the Saviour's birth.

— *Rev. Abram J. Ryan.*

A CHRISTMAS CAROL

I hear along our street
  Pass the minstrel throngs.
Hark! They play so sweet
  On their hautboys Christmas songs.
    Let us by the fire,
    Ever higher,
    Sing them till the night expire.

In December ring
  Every day the chimes;
Loud the glee men sing
  In the streets their merry rimes.
    Let us by the fire,
    Ever higher,
    Sing them till the night expire.

Shepherds at the grange,
  Where the Babe was born,
Sang with many a change
  Christmas carols until morn.
    Let us by the fire,
    Ever higher,
    Sing them till the night expire.

These good people sang
  Songs devout and sweet.
While the rafters rang
  There they stood with freezing feet.
    Let us by the fire,
    Ever higher,
    Sing them till the night expire.

Who by the fireside stands
  Stamps his feet and sings,
But he who blows his hands,
  Not so gay a carol brings.
    Let us by the fire,
    Ever higher,
    Sing them till the night expire.

— *Henry Wadsworth Longfellow.*

THE CROWDED INN

"There was no room for them in the inn" (St. Luke).

"Will ye take a stranger in?
  Dark the night is shrouded,
And the wintry blasts begin."
  "No; the inn is crowded."

"Will ye take a maiden in,
  Comes her hour of sorrow?
Long and late the way hath been!"
  "Wait until the morrow."

"Will ye take a baby in
  Out of cold and danger —
Mary's child of Kingly kin?"
  "Yonder is the manger."

Wilt thou take a Saviour in,
  Heart of sin and anguish,
With the peace of God to win —
  Wilt thou live or languish?

— *L. O. Williams.*

A CHRISTMAS CAROL

"What means this glory round our feet,"
    The Magi mused, "more bright than morn?"
And voices chanted clear and sweet,
    "Today the Prince of Peace is born!"

"What means that star," the shepherds said
    "That brightens through the rocky glen?"
And angels, answering overhead,
    Sang "Peace on earth, good will to men!"

'Tis eighteen hundred years and more
    Since those sweet oracles were dumb.
We wait for Him, like them of yore.
    Alas, He seems so slow to come!

But it was said in words of gold
    No time or sorrow e'er shall dim
That little children might be bold
    In perfect trust to come to Him.

All round about our feet shall shine
    A light like that the Wise Men saw
If we our loving wills incline
    To that sweet Life which is the law.

So shall we learn to understand
    The simple faith of shepherds then
And, clasping kindly hand in hand,
    Sing "Peace on earth, good will to men!"

And they who do their souls no wrong,
    But keep at eve the faith of morn,
Shall daily hear the angel song,
    "Today the Prince of Peace is born!"

— *James Russell Lowell.*

A CAROL

Of old, wise men to the manger came,
   Bearing their gifts, both precious and rare.
At the feet of an infant they laid them down
   As they breathed glad words of praise and prayer.
Of old, of old, in Bethlehem town
Wise men and kings laid their offerings down.

Of old, the shepherds on Judea's plains,
   Watching their flocks in the cheerless night,
Saw in the east a great Star shine,
   And they left their watch to follow its light.
Of old, of old, how bright the Star
That guided the wondering shepherds afar!

Of old, the voices of angel choirs
   Sang the joy of a Saviour's birth,
And the glory of God shone bright around
   As they chanted their message of "Peace on earth!"
Of old, great joy to the world was given
When Christ the Lord came down from heaven.

— A. J. Roberts, in *Chicago Herald*.

CHRISTMAS TIME

Some say that ever 'gainst that season comes,
Wherein our Saviour's birth is celebrated,
The bird of dawning singeth all night long,
And then, they say, no spirit dare stir abroad;
The nights are wholesome; then no planets strike,
No fairy takes, nor witch hath power to charm,
So hallowed and so gracious is the time.

— From Shakespeare's *Hamlet,* Act 1, Scene 1

[109]

THE LIGHT OF BETHLEHEM

'Tis Christmas Night! The snow
  A flock unnumbered lies;
The old Judean stars aglow
  Keep watch within the skies.

An icy stillness holds
  The pulses of the night;
A deeper mystery enfolds
  The wondering Hosts of Light.

Till lo, with reverence pale
  That dims each diadem,
The lordliest, earthward bending, hail
  The Light of Bethlehem!

— John Bannister Tabb.

SONGS RAISE ON HIGH

Sound over all waters, reach from all lands,
The chorus of voices, the clasping of hands;
  Sing hymns that were sung by the stars of the morn,
  Sing songs of the angel when Jesus was born!
      With glad jubilations
      Bring hope to the nations!
  The dark night is ending and dawn has begun;
  Rise, hope of the ages, arise like the sun,
  All speech flow to music, all hearts beat as one.
Blow, bugles of battle, the marches of peace;
East, west, north, and south, let the quarrels all cease,
  Sing the song of great joy that the angels began,
  Sing of glory to God and of good will to man!
      Hark, joining the chorus
      The heavens bend o'er us!

— John Greenleaf Whittier.

LORDLINGS, LISTEN TO OUR LAY

Lordlings, listen to our lay —
We have come from far away
  To seek Christmas;
In this mansion we are told
He His yearly feast doth hold:
  'Tis today!
May joy come from God above
To all those who Christmas love.

— *Old Carol*

CAROL OF CHRISTMAS

Day fades across the winter world;
  The snow is cold and deep;
Besides the window Christmas Eve
  Our twilight watch we keep.
O Christmas stars, O Christmas stars,
  Before our earnest eyes
You write the sweetest tale of earth
  Across the Christmas skies!

The wind drops down, the fields are still,
  The air is hushed and clear;
Far music trembles up the hill
  Upon our listening ear.
O Christmas bells, O Christmas bells,
  Ring silvery and long
Unto our little hearts you see
  The Christmas angels' song!

— Nancy Byrd Turner, in *Churchman.*

DELIGHTS OF CHRISTMAS
An Ancient Poem

When Christmas approaches each bosom is gay,
That festival banishes sorrow away,
While Richard he kisses both Susan and Dolly
When tricking the house up with ivy and holly,
For never as yet it was counted a crime
To be merry and cheery at that happy time.

Then come turkey and chine, with the famous roast beef,
Of English provisions still reckoned the chief.
Roger wishes the cook maid his wishes to crown,
"Oh, Dolly, pray give me a bit of the brown!"
For never as yet it was counted a crime
To be merry and cheery at that happy time.

The luscious plum pudding does smoking appear,
And the charming mince pie is not far from the rear.
Then each licks his chops to behold such a sight,
For to taste it affords him superior delight,
For never as yet it was counted a crime
To be merry and cheery at that happy time.

Now the humming October goes merrily round,
And each with good humor is happily crowned.
The song and the dance and the mirth-giving jest,
Alike without harm by each one is expressed.
For never as yet it was counted a crime
To be merry and cheery at that happy time.

Twelfth day next approaches to give you delight,
And the sugared rich cake is displayed to the sight;
The man and the maid and the king and the queen
Alike must be present to add to the scene,
For never as yet it was counted a crime
To be merry and cheery at that happy time.

May each be found thus as the year circles round,
With mirth and good humor each Christmas be crowned,
And may all who have plenty of riches in store
With their bountiful blessings make happy the poor,
For never as yet was it counted a crime
To be merry and cheery at that happy time.

— *Anonymous.*

AT CHRISTMAS EVE

Ah! there's nothing like a Christmas Eve
To change life's bitter gall to sweet,
And change the sweet to gall again;
To take the thorns from out our feet —
The thorns and all their dreary pain,
Only to put them back again.
To take old stings from out our heart —
Old stings that made them bleed and smart —
Only to sharpen them the more,
And press them back to the heart's core.

Ah! there's nothing like a Christmas Eve
To melt, with kindly glowing heart,
From off our souls the snow and sleet,
The dreary drift of wintry years,
Only to make the cold winds blow,
Only to make a colder snow;
And make it drift, and drift, and drift,
In flakes so icy cold and swift,
Until the heart that lies below
Is cold and colder than the snow.

— Rev. Abram Ryan, in *Philadelphia Record.*

A LEGEND OF CHRISTMAS

In sword and sash and scarlet coat
  Upon a Christmas day,
Through frosty woods and hoary fields
  A soldier rode away.
She watched him through the falling snow,
  A young and lovely maid
In milky pearls and flowing robes
  Of velvet green arrayed.

With rumors of the distant wars
  The months went slowly by
Till once again the Christmas bells
  Were pealing to the sky,
And, walking in the lonely wood,
  A bush the maiden found
With thorns as sharp as little swords
  And scarlet berries crowned.

She leaned against an ancient oak
  And wove a wreath to wear
Of scarlet berries, bright and gay,
  And set it on her hair.
And, lo, the pearls upon her breast
  Were changed to berries, too,
And, rooted to the oak, a branch
  Of mistletoe she grew.

When sweet and clear the Christmas bells
  Ring out o'er vale and hill
The maiden-mistletoe is seen
  In pearls and velvet still,
And with her in the revels ruled
  By music, mirth and folly.
In sword and scarlet still arrayed,
  Behold the soldier-holly!
          — Minna Irving, in *Leslie's*.

BEFORE THE PALING OF THE STARS

Before the paling of the stars,
  Before the winter morn,
Before the earliest cock-crow,
  Jesus Christ was born;
Born in a stable,
  Cradled in a manger.
In the world His hands had made,
  Born a stranger.

Priest and king lay fast asleep
  In Jerusalem.
Young and old lay fast asleep
  In crowded Bethlehem.
Saint and angel, ox and ass,
  Kept a watch together
Before the Christmas daybreak
  In the wintry weather.

Jesus on His Mother's breast
  In the stable cold,
Spotless Lamb of God was He,
  Shepherd of the fold;
Let us kneel with Mary Maid,
  With Joseph bent and hoary
With saint and angel, ox and ass,
  To hail the King of Glory.

— *Christina E. Rossetti.*

A VISIT FROM ST. NICHOLAS

'Twas the night before Christmas, when all through the house
Not a creature was stirring, not even a mouse;
The stockings were hung by the chimney with care,
In hopes that St. Nicholas soon would be there;
The children were nestled all snug in their beds,
While visions of sugar-plums danced in their heads;
And mamma in her kerchief and I in my cap,
Had just settled our brains for a long winter's nap, —
When out on the lawn there arose such a clatter,
I sprang from my bed to see what was the matter;
Away to the window I flew like a flash,
Tore open the shutters and threw up the sash.
The moon on the breast of the new-fallen snow,
Gave a luster of mid-day to objects below;
When, what to my wondering eyes should appear,
But a miniature sleigh and eight tiny reindeer,
With a little old driver, so lively and quick,
I knew in a moment it must be St. Nick.
More rapid than eagles his coursers they came,
And he whistled, and shouted, and called them by name:
"Now, Dasher! now, Dancer! now, Prancer and Vixen!
On! Comet, on! Cupid, on! Donder and Blitzen! —
To the top of the porch, to the top of the wall
Now, dash away, dash away, dash away all!"
As dry leaves that before the wild hurricane fly,
When they meet with an obstacle, mount to the sky,
So, to the housetop the coursers they flew
With the sleigh full of toys — and St. Nicholas, too.
And then in a twinkling I heard on the roof
The prancing and pawing of each little hoof.
As I drew in my head, and was turning around,
Down the chimney St. Nicholas came with a bound.
He was dressed all in fur from his head to his foot,
And his clothes were all tarnished with ashes and soot;

A bundle of toys he had flung on his back,
And he looked like a peddler just opening his pack.
His eyes how they twinkled! his dimples how merry;
His cheeks were like roses, his nose like a cherry;
His droll little mouth was drawn up like a bow,
And the beard on his chin was as white as the snow.
The stump of a pipe he held tight in his teeth,
And the smoke, it encircled his head like a wreath.
He was chubby and plump — a right jolly old elf;
And I laughed when I saw him, in spite of myself.
A wink of his eye, and twist of his head
Soon gave me to know I had nothing to dread.
He spoke not a word, but went straight to his work,
And filled all the stockings; then turned with a jerk,
And laying his finger aside of his nose,
And giving a nod, up the chimney he rose.
He sprang to his sleigh, to his team gave a whistle,
And away they all flew like the down of a thistle;
But I heard him exclaim, ere he drove out of sight:
"Happy Christmas to all, and to all a good-night."

— Clement C. Moore.

NO ROOM FOR THEM

O foolish folk, what blindness held your sight,
    O heedless folk of olden Bethlehem!
Could ye but know who sought a place that night,
    I ween ye had found room enough for them!
O Christian men, O Christian maids and wives!
    How can ye blame the folks of Bethlehem,
If God's elect are strangers in your lives,
    If in your hearts you have no room for them!

— Denis A. McCarthy.

[117]

WHEN CHRISTMAS COMES

When Christmas comes I never mind the cold.
 I like to get up prompt an' go to school
  An' do my sums
An' clean the walks 'thout waitin' to be told,
 Though I like sleddin' better, as a rule,
Or buildin' forts — but nothin' ain't so bad
 When Christmas comes.

When Christmas comes I'd just as lief give half
 My cooky to the baby an' take care
  About the crumbs.
It's fun to make the little fellow laugh,
 An' I don't mind his taggin' ev'rywhere.
He can't help bein' little. I'm not mad
 When Christmas comes.

When Christmas comes I don't forget to give
 My shoes a wipe an' scrub my ears a lot
  Till my head hums.
An' mother says, "That boy's too good to live."
 But I'm not 'fraid of dyin', cause I'm not
No different from always — only glad
 When Christmas comes.

— Abigail Burton, in *St. Nicholas*.

BURNING BABE

As I in hoary winter's night stood shivering in the snow,
Surprised I was with sudden heat, which made my heart to glow!
And lifting up a fearful eye to view what fire was near,
A pretty Babe, all burning bright, did in the air appear,
Who scorched with excessive heat, such floods of tears did shed,
As though His floods should quench His flames, with which his
 tears were fed.

"Alas!" quoth He, "but newly born, in fiery heat I fry.
Yet none approach to warm their hearts or feel My fire but I!
My faultless breast the furnace is, the fuel wounding thorns.
Love is the fire, and sighs the smoke, the ashes shame and scorns.
The fuel Justice layeth on, and Mercy blows the coals.
The metals in this furnace wrought are men's defiled souls,
For which, as now on fire I am, to work them to their good.
So will I melt into a bath to wash them in My blood."
With these He vanished out of sight and swiftly shrunk away,
And straight I called unto mind that it was Christmas Day.

— *Robert Southwell, Martyr Poet*
(Executed Tyburn, 1595)

THE WEEK BEFORE CHRISTMAS

'Tis the week before Christmas and every night,
    As soon as the children are snuggled up tight
And have sleepily murmured their wishes and prayers,
    Such fun as goes on in the parlor downstairs!
For Father, Big Brother and Grandfather too,
    Start in with great vigor their youth to renew.
The games are unwrapped and directions are read
    And they play till it's long past their hour for bed.

They try to solve puzzles and each one enjoys
    The magical thrill of mechanical toys.
Even Mother must play with a doll that can talk,
    And if you assist it, is able to walk.
It's really no matter if paint may be scratched,
    Or a cog wheel, a nut, or a bolt gets detached;
The grown-ups are having great fun — all is well;
    The children don't know it, and Santa won't tell.

"IF I WERE SANTA CLAUS"

If I were Santa Claus,
  I'd pass the boys
And give the little girls
  The nicest toys.
If I were Santa Claus.

If I were Santa Claus,
  To one I know
A doll that falls asleep
  And talks would go;
If I were Santa Claus.

If I were Santa Claus,
  In Bobby's socks
I'd put old ashes and
  Big frozen rocks;
If I were Santa Claus.

If I were Santa Claus,
  And had my way,
I'd make him pull me on
  His sled all day;
If I were Santa Claus.

If I were Santa Claus,
  I'd stay up late
And by the parlor fire
  Would sit and wait;
If I were Santa Claus.

If I were Santa Claus,
  For that plump elf —
But, oh, how could I? For
  He'd be myself;
If I were Santa Claus.

  — G. H. Barbour.

SOMETHING WRONG

If you've lost your zest for Christmas,
  Lost your love for all its cheer;
If you scoff at gifts and giving
  As the Christmas time draws near,
If you frown at all the clatter
  When old Santa trims his tree,
Tell me, please, what is the matter?
  Something's wrong, it seems to me!

If the stocking by the hearthstone
  Wakes no memory in your breast,
If the coming of old Santa
  After all have gone to rest
Does not arouse your heart to action,
  Make it beat and throb and kick,
Answer for my satisfaction,
  Are you sure you are not sick?

If you can't feel joy at Christmas,
  Joy of life and joy of song;
If you can't rejoice in giving,
  Whether it be right or wrong;
If the Yule log's invitation
  To your heart no cheer can give,
Let me ask how in creation
  Is it worth your while to live?
        — Lurana Sheldon, in *New York Times*.

All children love the following rhyme:
"LITTLE JACK HORNER"

Little Jack Horner, sat in a corner,
  Eating his Christmas pie,
He put in his thumb and pulled out a plum,
  And said, "What a good boy am I."

FOLLOWING THE STAR

It was the eve of Christmas; the snow lay deep and white.
I sat beside my window and looked into the night.
I heard the church bells ringing, I saw the bright stars shine,
And childhood came again to me with all its dreams divine.
Then as I listened to the bells and watched the skies afar,
Out of the east majestic there rose one radiant star,
And every other star grew pale before that heavenly glow.
It seemed to bid me follow, and I could not choose but go.

From street to street it led me by many a mansion fair.
It shone through dingy casements on many a garret bare,
From highway on to highway, through alleys dark and cold,
And where it shone the darkness was flooded all with gold.
Sad hearts forgot their sorrow, rough hearts grew soft and mild,
And weary little children turned in their sleep and smiled,
While many a homeless wanderer uplifted patient eyes,
Seeming to see a home at last beyond those starry skies.

And then methought earth faded. I rose as borne on wings
Beyond the waste of ruined lives, the press of human things.
Above the toil and shadow, above the want and woe,
My old self and its darkness seemed left on earth below,
And onward, upward, shone the star until it seemed to me
It flashed upon the golden gates and o'er the crystal sea,
And then the gates rolled backwards; I stood where angels trod.
It was the Star of Bethlehem had led me up to God.

— Frederic E. Weatherly.

THE SHEPHERDS' HYMN

Come, we shepherds, whose blest sight
    Hath met Love's moon in nature's night;
Come, lift we up our loftier song,
    And wake the sun that lies too long!

Gloomy night embraced the place
   Where the noble Infant lay.
The Babe looked up and showed His face;
   In spite of darkness, it was day.
   It was Thy day, Sweet! and did rise,
   Not from the East, but from Thine eyes.

We saw Thee in Thy balmy nest,
   Young dawn of our eternal Day!
We saw Thine eyes break from their east
   And chase the trembling shades away.
   We saw Thee; and we blest the sight;
   We saw Thee by Thine own sweet light.

Poor world (said I), what wilt thou do
   To entertain this starry Stranger?
Is this the best thou canst bestow?
   A cold, and not too cleanly, manger?
   Contend, the powers of Heaven and Earth,
   To fit a bed for this huge birth!

— From "A Hymn Sung as by the Shepherds,"
    by Richard Crashaw (1649).

AN OLD POEM

With holly and ivy
   So green and so gay
We deck up our houses
   As fresh as the day;

With bay and rosemary
   And laurel complete;
And everyone now
   Is a queen in conceit.

— Old Poem, 1695

[123]

CHRISTMAS

Ring out, ye joyful Christmas chime,
Glad songs to ev'ry land and clime!
  Nor cease your merry peals until
The message wond'ring shepherds heard
The hearts of all mankind has stirred —
  "Peace on earth; to men good will!"

Ring out, ye joyful Christmas bell!
Let ev'ry rich note gladly tell
  That war and blood-lust both shall cease
When men in truth accept the sway
Of Him born on this Christmas Day —
  The manger-cradled Prince of Peace.

Ring out the demons Hate and Might!
Ring in the angels Love and Right!
  Bid Freedom, prostrate on the ground,
Arise and face the golden morn
Whereon the Prince of Peace was born —
  And shout for joy to hear your sound.

Ring out, ye merry Christmas chime,
And usher in the glad New Time
  When, with the royal diadem,
All men have come with joyful sound,
And in true love as King have crowned
  The Blessed Babe of Bethlehem.

CHRISTMAS BELLS

I heard the bells on Christmas Day
Their old familiar carols play,
And wild and sweet the words repeat
Of peace on earth, good will to men!

I thought how, as the day had come,
The Belfries of all Christendom
Had rolled along the unbroken song
Of peace on earth, good will to men!

And in despair I bowed my head;
"There is no peace on earth," I said,
"For hate is strong, and mocks the song
Of peace on earth, good will to men."

Then pealed the bells more loud and deep,
"God is not dead, nor doth he sleep!
The wrong shall fail, the right prevail,
With peace on earth, good will to men!"

Till, ringing, singing on its way,
The world revolved from night to day,
A voice, a chime, a chant sublime,
Of peace on earth, good will to men!

— *Henry Wadsworth Longfellow.*

THE BIRTH OF CHRIST

The time draws near the birth of Christ;
  The moon is hid; the night is still;
  The Christmas bells from hill to hill
Answer each other in the mist.

Four voices of four hamlets round,
  From far and near, on mead and moor,
  Swell out and fail as if a door
Were shut between me and the sound.

Each voice four changes of the wind,
  That now dilate, and now decrease,
  Peace and goodwill, goodwill and peace,
Peace and goodwill, to all mankind.

Rise, happy morn, rise, holy morn,
  Draw forth the cheerful day from night;
  O Father, touch the East, and light
The light that shone when Hope was born.

— *Tennyson*

CHRISTMAS CAROLS

SILENT NIGHT

Silent night, Holy night,
All is dark, save the light,
Yonder, where they sweet vig-
ils keep,
O'er the Babe, who in silent
sleep,
Rests in heavenly peace,
Rests in heavenly peace.

2

Silent, night, Peaceful night,
Darkness flies, all is light;
Shepherds hear the angels sing,
Alleluia! Hail the King,
Christ the Saviour is born,
Christ the Saviour is born.

3

Silent night, Holy night,
Child of heaven, Oh how bright,
Was Thy smile, when Thou
wast born,
Blest indeed that happy morn,

Full of heavenly joy,
Full of heavenly joy.

STILLE NACHT

Stille Nacht, Heilige Nacht,
Alles schläft, einsam wacht,
Nur das traute hochheilige
Paar,
Holder Knabe im lockigen
Haar,
Schlaf in himmlischer Ruh,
Schlaf in himmlischer Ruh.

2

Stille Nacht, Heilige Nacht,
Hirten erst, kund gemacht,
Durch der Engel Halleluja,
Tönt es laut von fern und nah,
Christ, der Retter ist da,
Christ, der Retter ist da.

3

Stille Nacht, Heilige Nacht,
Gottes Sohn, O wie lacht,
Lieb aus deinem Göttlichen
Mund,
Da uns schlagt die rettende
Stund,
Christ in deiner Geburt,
Christ in deiner Geburt.

"ADESTE FIDELES"

O come, all ye faithful
  Joyfully triumphant,
O come ye, O come ye,
  to Bethlehem.
Come and behold Him,
Born, the King of Angels.
Chorus:
O come, let us adore Him,
  O come, let us adore Him.
O come, let us adore Him,
  Christ, the Lord.

2

Angels now praise Him,
  Loud their voices raising
The heavenly mansions with
  joy now ring,
  Praise, honor, glory,
To Him who is most holy.
Chorus:

"ADESTE FIDELES"

Adeste, fideles,
  Laeti triumphantes,
Venite, venite, ad Bethlehem.

  Natum videte,
Regem angelorum.
Chorus:
Venite adoremus,
  Venite adoremus.
Venite adoremus,
  dominum.

2

Cantet nunc hymnos,
  Chorus Angelorum
Cantet nunc aula caelestium

  Gloria, Gloria,
In excelsis Deo.
Chorus:

HARK! THE HERALD ANGELS SING

Hark! the herald angels sing,
  "Glory to the newborn King!
Peace on earth and mercy mild,
  God and sinners reconciled."
Joyful, all ye nations rise,
  Join the triumph of the skies;
With th' angelic host proclaim,
  "Christ is born in Bethlehem."
Chorus:
Hark! the herald angels sing,
  "Glory to the newborn King!"

WHILE SHEPHERDS WATCHED THEIR FLOCKS BY NIGHT

While shepherds watched their flocks by night:
All seated on the ground,
The angel of the Lord came down,
And glory shone around,
And glory shone around.

2

"Fear not," said he, for mighty dread
Had seized their troubled mind,
"Glad tidings of great joy I bring,
To you and all mankind,
To you and all mankind."

3

"All glory be to God on high,
And to the earth be peace;
Goodwill henceforth from heav'n to men,
Begin and never cease,
Begin and never cease."

CRADLE HYMN

Away in a manger, no crib for a bed,
The little Lord Jesus laid down His sweet head;
The stars in the sky looked down where He lay,
The little Lord Jesus, asleep on the hay.
The cattle are lowing, the poor Baby wakes,
But little Lord Jesus, no crying He makes;
I love Thee, Lord Jesus, look down from the sky,
And stay by my cradle to watch lullaby.

ANGELS FROM THE REALMS OF GLORY

Angels from the realms of glory,
  Wing your flight o'er all the earth;
Ye, who sang creation's story,
  Now proclaim Messiah's birth.
Chorus:
Come and worship! Come and worship!
  Worship Christ, the newborn King!

2

Shepherds in the field abiding,
  Watching o'er your flocks by night,
God with man is now residing,
  Yonder shines the infant light.
Chorus:

3

Sages, leave your contemplations,
  Brighter visions beam afar;
Seek the great Desire of nations,
  Ye have seen His natal star.
Chorus:

THE FIRST NOEL

The first Noel, the angel did say,
Was to certain poor shepherds in fields as they lay;
In fields where they lay keeping their sheep,
On a cold winter's night that was so deep.
Chorus:
Noel, Noel, Noel, Noel!
Born is the King of Israel!

2

They looked up and saw a star,
Shining in the East, beyond them far,
And to the earth it gave great light,
And so it continued both day and night.
Chorus:

And by the light of that same star,
Three wise men came from country far;
To seek for a king was their intent,
And to follow the star wherever it went.
Chorus:

DECK THE HALL

Deck the halls with boughs of holly,
    Fa la la la la, la la la la.
'Tis the season to be jolly,
    Fa la la la la, la la la la.
Don we now our gay apparel,
    Fa la la la la, la la.
Troll the ancient Yuletide carol,
    Fa la la la la, la la la la.

2

See the blazing Yule before us,
    Fa la la la la, la la la la.
Strike the harp and join the chorus,
    Fa la la la la, la la la la.
Follow me in merry measure,
    Fa la la la la, la la.
While I tell of Yuletide treasure,
    Fa la la la la, la la la la.

3

Fast away the old year passes,
    Fa la la la la, la la la la.
Hail the new, ye lads and lassies.
    Fa la la la la, la la la la.
Sing we joyous all together,
    Fa la la la la, la la.
Heedless of the wind and weather.
    Fa la la la la, la la la la.

GOD REST YOU MERRY GENTLEMEN

God rest you merry gentlemen,
  Let nothing you dismay,
Remember Christ, our Saviour
  Was born on Christmas day:
To save us all from Satan's power
  When we were gone astray.
Chorus:
Oh, tidings of comfort and joy, comfort and joy,
Oh, tidings of comfort and joy.

2

In Bethlehem in Jewry,
  This Blessed Babe was born,
And laid within a manger
  Upon this blessed morn:
The which His Mother Mary
  Did nothing take in scorn.
Chorus:

3

From God our heavenly Father
  A blessed angel came,
And unto certain shepherds
  Brought tidings of the same:
How that in Bethlehem was born
  The Son of God by name.
Chorus:

4

Fear not them, said the angel,
  Let nothing you affright,
This day is born a Saviour
  Of a pure virgin bright.
To free all those who trust in Him,
  From Satan's power and might.
Chorus:

O TANNENBAUM
(German Folk Song)

O Tannenbaum, O Tannenbaum,
Wie grün sind deine Blätter?
O Tannenbaum, O Tannenbaum,
Wie grün sind deine Blätter?
Du grünst nicht nur zur Som-
    merzeit,
Nein auch im Winter, wenn es
    schneit
O Tannenbaum, O Tannenbaum,
Wie grün sind deine Blätter?

2

O Tannenbaum, O Tannenbaum,
Du kannst mir sehr gefallen.
O Tannenbaum, O Tannenbaum,
Du kannst mir sehr gefallen.
Wie oft hat schon zur Weih-
    nachtszeit,
Ein Baum von dir mich hoch
    erfreut.
O Tannenbaum, O Tannenbaum,
Du kannst mir sehr gefallen.

3

O Tannenbaum, O Tannenbaum,
Dein Kleid will mich was lehren.
O Tannenbaum, O Tannenbaum,
Dein Kleid will mich was lehren.
Die Hoffnung und Beständigkeit,
Gibt Trost und Kraft zu jeder
    Zeit,
O Tannenbaum, O Tannenbaum,
Das soll dein Kleid mich lehren.

O EVERGREEN

O Evergreen, O Evergreen,
How are thy leaves so
    verdant?
O Evergreen, O Evergreen,
How are thy leaves so
    verdant?
Not only in the summertime,
But e'en in winter is thy
    prime,
O Evergreen, O Evergreen,
How are thy leaves so
    verdant?

2

O Evergreen, O Evergreen,
We sing in happy measure.
O Evergreen, O Evergreen,
We sing in happy measure.
Thy praise who dost our
    Christmas greet,
With verdure fair and mem'-
    ries sweet,
O Evergreen, O Evergreen,
Tree of unfailing treasure.

3

O Evergreen, O Evergreen,
Thy garb unfading showeth,
O Evergreen, O Evergreen,
Thy garb unfading showeth,
The flow'r of joy about my
    door,
Good cheer that faileth never
    more,
O Evergreen, O Evergreen,
My heart thy lesson knoweth.

UP ON THE HOUSETOP

Up on the housetop reindeer pause,
Out jumps good old Santa Claus;
Down through the chimney with lots of toys,
All for the little ones, Christmas joys.
Chorus:
Ho, ho, ho! who wouldn't go!
Ho, ho, ho! who wouldn't go!
Up on the housetop, click, click, click,
Down through the chimney with good Saint Nick.

2

First comes the stocking of little Nell;
Oh, dear Santa, fill it well:
Give her a dollie that laughs and cries,
One that will open and shut her eyes.
Chorus:

3

Next comes the stocking of little Will;
Oh, just see what a glorious fill!
Here is a hammer and lots of tacks,
Also a ball and a whip that cracks.
Chorus:

SANTA CLAUS

There's a jolly little fellow
    Who comes riding into town.
When the north wind blows his trumpet,
    And the snow comes dancing down;
In a coat of fur and ermine,
    He is muffled to his chin,
And his face, whate'er the weather,
    Always wears a pleasant grin.

He's a friend of all the children
  For he carries on his back,
Gifts to make their bright eyes sparkle
  Safely stowed within his pack;
And they always hang their stockings
  By the fireplace because
Christmas Eve is sure to bring them
  Presents from old Santa Claus.

GOOD KING WENCESLAUS

Good King Wenceslaus looked out
  On the Feast of Stephen,
When the snow lay round about,
  Deep, crisp and even:
Brightly shone the moon that night,
  Though the frost was cruel,
When a poor man came in sight,
  Gathering winter fuel.

2

"Hither, page, and stand by me,
  If thou know'st it, telling,
Yonder peasant, who is he?
  Where and what his dwelling?"
"Sire, he lives a good leage hence,
  Underneath the mountain;
Right against the forest fence,
  By Saint Agnes' fountain."

3

In his master's step he trod,
  Where the snow lay dinted;
Heat was in the very sod
  Which the saint had printed.
Therefore, Christian men, be sure
  Wealth or rank possessing,
Ye who now will bless the poor,
  Shall yourself find blessing.

O LITTLE TOWN OF BETHLEHEM

O little town of Bethlehem,
  How still we see thee lie!
Above thy deep and dreamless sleep
  The silent stars go by.
Yet in thy dark streets shineth
  The everlasting light;
The hopes and fears of all the years
  Are met in thee tonight.

2

For Christ is born of Mary,
  And gather'd all above,
While mortals sleep, the angels keep
  Their watch of wond'ring love.
O morning stars together,
  Proclaim the holy birth!
And praises sing to God, the King,
  And peace to men on earth.

3

How swiftly and how silently,
  The wondrous gift is giv'n!
So God imparts to human hearts
  The blessings of His heav'n.
No ear may hear His coming,
  But in this world of sin,
Where meek souls will receive Him still,
  The dear Christ enters in.

4

O holy Child of Bethlehem!
  Descend to us, we pray;
Cast out our sin, and enter in;
  Be born in us today.
We hear the Christmas angels
  The great, glad tidings tell;
Oh, come to us, abide with us,
  Our Lord Emmanuel.

JINGLE BELLS

Dashing through the snow
In a one-horse open sleigh,
O'er the fields we go,
Laughing all the way;
Bells on bobtail ring,
Making spirits bright,
What fun it is to ride and sing
A sleighing song tonight!
Chorus:
Jingle bells! jingle bells!
Jingle all the way!
Oh, what fun it is to ride
In a one-horse open sleigh!

(*Repeat*)

2

A day or two ago
I thought I'd take a ride,
And soon Miss Fannie Bright
Was seated by my side;
The horse was lean and lank,
Misfortune seemed his lot,
He got into a drifted bank,
And we got upsot.
Chorus:

3

Now the ground is white,
To it while you're young,
Take the girls out tonight,
And sing this sleighing song;
Just get a bobtailed nag,
Two-forty for his speed,
Then hitch him to an open sleigh,
And crack! you'll take the lead.
Chorus:

IT CAME UPON A MIDNIGHT CLEAR

It came upon a midnight clear,
    That glorious song of old,
From angels bending near the earth,
    To touch their harps of gold;
Peace on the earth, good will to men,
    From heaven's all gracious King;
The world in solemn stillness lay
    To hear the angels sing.

2

Still through the cloven skies they come,
    With peaceful wings unfurled;
And still their heavenly music floats
    O'er all the weary world;
Above its sad and lowly plains
    They bend on hovering wing,
And ever o'er its Babel sounds
    The blessed angels sing.

3

O ye, beneath life's crushing load,
    Whose forms are bending low,
Who toil along the climbing way
    With painful steps and slow,
Look now, for glad and golden hours
    Come swiftly on the wing;
O rest beside the weary road,
    And hear the angels sing.

4

For lo! the days are hastening on,
    By prophets seen of old,
When with the ever-circling years,
    Shall come the time foretold,
When the new heaven and earth shall own
    The Prince of Peace their King,
And the whole world send back the song
    Which now the angels sing.

JOY TO THE WORLD

Joy to the world! the Lord is come;
Let earth receive her King;
Let every heart prepare Him room,
And heav'n and nature sing,
And heav'n and nature sing,
And heav'n and heav'n and nature sing.

2

Joy to the world! the Saviour reigns;
Let men their songs employ.
While fields and floods, rocks, hills, and plains,
Repeat the sounding joy,
Repeat the sounding joy,
Repeat, repeat the sounding joy.

3

No more let sin and sorrow grow,
Nor thorns infest the ground;
He comes to make His blessings flow
Far as the curse is found,
Far as the curse is found,
Far as, far as the curse is found.

4

He rules the world with truth and grace,
And makes the nations prove
The glories of His righteousness
And wonders of His love,
And wonders of His love,
And wonders, wonders of His love.

WE THREE KINGS OF ORIENT ARE

We three kings of Orient are;
Bearing gifts we traverse far
Field and fountain, moor and mountain,
Following yonder Star.
CHORUS:
O Star of wonder, Star of night,
Star with royal beauty bright,
Westward leading still proceeding,
Guide us to Thy perfect light.

2

Melchior:
Born a King on Bethlehem's plain
Gold I bring to crown Him again,
King forever ceasing never,
Over us all to reign.

3

Casper:
Frankincense to offer have I,
Incense owns a Deity nigh,
Pray'r and praising, all men raising,
Worship Him, God most High.

4

Balthazar:
Myrrh is mine, its bitter perfume
Breathes a life of gathering gloom,
Sorrowing, sighing, bleeding, dying,
Seal'd in the stone-cold tomb.

5

Glorious now behold Him arise,
King and God and sacrifice,
Alleluia, Alleluia,
Earth to heav'n replies.

O HOLY NIGHT
(*Cantique de Noel*)

O holy night the stars are brightly shining,
    It is the night of the dear Saviour's birth;
Long lay the world in sin and error pining,
    Till He appeared and the soul felt its worth,
A thrill of hope the weary world rejoices,
    For yonder breaks a new and glorious morn.
Fall on your knees, Oh, hear the angel voices.
    O night divine, O night when Christ was born!
O night, O holy night, O night divine.

Led by the light of faith serenely beaming
With glowing hearts by His cradle we stand;
    So led by light of stars sweetly gleaming,
Here came the wise men from Orient land,
    The King of Kings lay thus in lowly manger,
In all trials born to be our friend;
    He knows our need, to our weakness is no stranger
Behold your King — Before Him lowly bend
    Behold your King — Before Him lowly bend!

OH COME LITTLE CHILDREN	IHR KINDERLEIN KOMMET
1	**1**
Oh come little children from cot and from hall,	Ihr Kinderlein kommet, o kommet doch all,
Oh come to the manger, in Bethlehem's stall,	Zur Krippe her kommet in Bethlehem's Stall,
There meekly He lieth, the heavenly Child,	Und seht, was in dieser hochheiligen Nacht
So poor and so humble, so sweet and so mild.	Der Vater im Himmel für Freude uns macht.
2	**2**
The hay is His pillow, the manger His bed,	O seht in der Krippe, im finsteren Stall,

The beasts stand in wonder, to
    gaze on His head.
Yet there where He lieth, so
    weak and so poor,
Come shepherd and wiseman to
    kneel at His door.

3

Now Glory to God: sing the
    angels on high,
And peace upon earth;
    heav'nly voices reply.
Then come little children and
    join in the lay
That gladdened the world on
    that fair Christmas Day.

Seht hier bei des Lichtlein's
    hellglänzendem Strahl,
In reinlichen Windeln das
    himmlische Kind,
Viel schöner und holder als
    Engel es sind.

3

Dort liegt es, das Kindlein, auf
    Heu and auf Stroh,
Maria und Josef betrachten es
    froh,
Die redlichen Hirten knieen be-
    tend davor;
Hoch oben schwebt Jubel der
    Engel empor.

APPENDIX

Bethlehem Today
and
Christmas Pictures

BETHLEHEM

Bethlehem Today

Peace and tranquillity hover over Bethlehem and the neighborhood the same as when the Christmas angel announced his message of glad tidings and "peace on earth." The field, where two thousand years ago, shepherds watched their flocks by night, is now enclosed with a wall and is a paradise of olive trees. The rustic folk carry on habits of life as it was lived years ago. Sheep and goats still roam the fields, sowers still sow the seed by hand, and maids carry water jars on their heads. They still plow in Bethlehem with a low, single-handled, wooden contraption hitched to oxen or camels. Bethlehem, as a city, has a population of nearly 10,000, of which 9,700 are Christians, 300 Moslems, and scarcely a dozen Jews. It is an assembly of limestone dwellings, markets, and cobbly streets flanked with souvenir shops. Situated on two ridges, Bethlehem is altogether enchanting and retains a spirit of legend. Monastic buildings, cloistered walls, arches, barred windows, and dipping streets contribute to this general effect. There is a primitive simplicity of living with little privacy along the streets.

Shops that have no windows flank the little hilly thoroughfares. Within we find miniature wooden camel ink-wells carved of olive wood, star breast pins, tiny carved mangers for holding stamps, rosaries of pearl and olive seeds, and the like, which are not only sold for souvenirs, but are actually manufactured on the premises. In the public squares and market, we find pots and pans for domestic purposes, while the pyramids of cucumbers and fruits proclaim the taste of the Bethlehemite.

But we must cross the threshold of a home to see how picturesquely the natives live. The dwellings in the older part of the town are a counterpart of the ones in Christ's time, with rooms above a grotto stable. The modern shepherd of Bethlehem brings his flock indoors at night, instead of camping under the stars. The so-called "modern" house of white stone contains a suite of rooms and a kitchen with a large oven where bread and platters of rice minced with grape leaves are baked. Luxurious Turkish rugs of glorious hues cover the stone floor while couches are indispensable. Coffee is the popular beverage of Palestine. Cucumbers stuffed with meat, sour goat's milk and dishes garnished with ripe olives are favorites with them.

Styles never change. The babe is still wrapped in "swaddling clothes" even as was the Divine Infant. The children wear loose sack-fitting clothes and are happy in bare feet. The Bethlehem women, with Madonna countenances, are mostly blondes and noted for their simple beauty. Their huge skirts and sleeves of black sateen are gorgeously embroidered and a sash or belt is worn at the waist; over their dresses they also wear jackets exquisitely embroidered. All women wear this same style of costume but their headdress varies. The unmarried woman wears a "halo" of coins punctured and fastened to a veil of embroidered white cotton. The married women's headdress is built upon a fez, over which the white drapery falls, covering the shoulders.

The mother-of-pearl industry in which primitive tiny tools are used is the outstanding trade of Bethlehem. Exquisite pearl designs are unequaled by artisans elsewhere. This industry with the allied arts of stone and wood carving that turn Dead Sea stones, and olive and sandal wood into rosaries, crosses, and jewelry, provides occupation for almost every hand. This trade has existed for several centuries. The finished product is the result of community effort, as each worker is skilled in his own special kind of manipulation. Bethlehem is now a prosperous town and its inhabitants are thought to be descended from the Crusaders with an admixture of Syrian and Arabic blood. During the last few decades, a great percentage of the youths leave their homes and go abroad, especially to North and South America, where they generally prosper and then return to Bethlehem with their gains to build costly houses.

The chief interest of Bethlehem centers around the basilica under which lies that shrine of shrines — the Grotto of the Nativity. The basilica, built in A.D. 330 by Constantine, is one of the oldest churches in the world. Its location is accepted by even the most skeptical as the most likely site for the holy inn and stable, as in early times it was the end of the main road leading into town. The basilica is noted for its dwarf entrance — its "needle eye" door, five feet high. From fear of assault in war time, and to prevent horses from being brought into the basilica, this small passage gives access to the body of the building. This part is a rectangle 100 feet long by 70 feet wide and is divided into five aisles by four rows of pillars. The transept is as wide as the central aisle and terminates on the north and south in two semicircular apses, which jut out from the main body of the building.

The Greeks own the high altar and the south arm, and the Armenians the north arm. Underneath the central portion of the transept is the Grotto of the Nativity.

Originally the Grotto must have been above ground. It is 42 feet long by 12 feet wide and 10 feet high, and is lighted by 32 gold and silver thurible-shaped lamps, representing the Armenian, Latin, and Greek denominations. The walls and floors are covered with marble. In the floor is a silver star bearing the simple Latin inscription *Hic de Virgine Maria Jesus Christus natus est*. According to ancient tradition this is the exact place where the Blessed Virgin gave birth to the Saviour of men. Around the star, burn day and night, fifteen lamps, of which four belong to the Latins, five to the Armenians, and six to the Greeks. More than once this star has been torn off or stolen, once by the Greeks in 1847 who restored it in 1852. Only about 25 years ago some of the nails which hold the star in place disappeared and naturally had to be replaced. But what sect should replace them? Finally, a gypsy Mohammedan silversmith was called in to make the repairs. To him no one had any objection. This spot was highly decorated as far back as the time of Constantine, and a few ancient mosaics are still visible.

Opposite the star, and three steps lower, is the Oratory of the Manger. Here it was that the Virgin Mother laid her newborn Son on the straw and here also the shepherds directed by the angels came to adore the Messiah. The spot is marked now by a marble manger containing the wax figure of an infant, and hung with lamps. In this same chapel has been erected an altar dedicated to the Wise Men from the East, who, guided by a star, came to prostrate themselves on this spot. The linoleum draping of the wall was put in to prevent relic seekers from cutting off pieces of the rock as souvenirs.

At one end of the underground passage is seen a circular hole from which water bubbled miraculously out of the ground for the special needs of the Holy Family. A pretty legend attaches to this well. It is said that the Magi star dropped into it and that it is visible only to virgins.

At the end of the Grotto of the Nativity is found the place where, it is said, Joseph received the warning from the angel who commanded him to set out for Egypt.

A few steps lead to the Chapel of the Holy Innocents. A tradition of the fifteenth century places here the scene of the murder by Herod of some infants who had been concealed for safety by their mothers. It is here the beautiful hymn, *Salvete Flores Martyrum* "All Hail ye Little Martyr Flowers" is sung by the children's choir of Bethlehem: "All hail, ye little martyr flowers whom, on the very threshold of light, the persecution of Christ has cut down, like the tender rosebuds scattered by a whirlwind. O, ye first victims for Christ, tender lambs immolated for Him, with childlike innocence, ye play, even under the altar, with your palms and crowns."

St. Jerome's chapel completes the suite of underground chambers sacred to Christ and His first few days on earth.

The original manger is now preserved in the Church of St. Mary Major in Rome, where it was taken in the twelfth century. The remains of the crib preserved there consist of five pieces of board taken from a sycamore tree of which there are several varieties in the Holy Land. Properly speaking, these pieces of wood were most likely supports for the manger itself, which was probably made from the soft limestone of which the cave was formed. The relics are preserved in a rich reliquary of silver and are solemnly exposed for the veneration of the faithful each year on the eve of Christmas.

Long before midnight the pilgrims (and tourists) arrive in Bethlehem for the Christmas celebration. It is customary to emulate the pilgrims of old and march in procession from Jerusalem (six miles away) chanting as they march. The parish church of St. Catherine adjoining the ancient Nativity Basilica itself, of which the Catholics have been deprived since 1637, fills gradually. It is here that the Patriarch, garbed in gorgeous vestments, says the Pontifical Mass, to accommodate the vast crowd, while in the grotto itself, Midnight Mass is said by the Franciscan parish priest of Bethlehem whose privilege it is to say these Midnight Masses. The wax image of the Christ Child is exposed above the tabernacle in the church during the Mass said by the Patriarch, and after its conclusion the Patriarch carries it in procession through the church and into the basilica, down the steps into the grotto where it is placed in the manger. The services are then concluded.

Close to the place in Bethlehem where Jesus was born is a grotto in which the Holy Family took refuge before starting out for Egypt to escape the persecution of Herod. According to a very ancient tradition, a few drops of Mary's virginal milk fell to the ground while she was giving breast to her Divine Babe, and gave to the grotto a wonderful power. From the earliest times a custom has obtained that when mothers have lacked milk while nursing, after drinking of water with a little of the powdered ground from the rock of the grotto, they have felt the desired increase of nourishment for their little babes. This belief is shared by the Christians and Moslems alike.

Near Bethlehem is a vast field covered with innumerable little pebbles. One day a man was sowing dwarf peas in that field, says a legend, when Jesus passing by asked him, "What are you sowing there, my friend?" "Stones," was the answer. "Very well, you will reap stones." And truly, when the sower came to gather them, he found nothing but petrified peas.

Bethlehem has three Christmases. First, there is the elaborate Latin or Roman Catholic service, which takes place on December 25. It is followed thirteen days later by the Greek Christmas services, as they keep the old calendar; then thirteen days later, by the Christmas services of the Armenian Church.

Although in northern countries we associate snow with the Christmas crib, it is a fact that snow rarely falls in Bethlehem and there is no evidence that it fell at the time our Lord was born.

The ancient name of Bethlehem was Beit Lahm, meaning house of bread. The name is no less striking for its spiritual significance, Bethlehem being the place where the world's "Bread of Life" was brought forth. In this connection it is interesting to note that the primeval wheat, which is the original of the cultivated wheat, has been found wild only in this country.

During the summer of 1934 excavations were conducted by the British government in the interior of the Basilica of the Nativity, with the consent of the Catholic, Greek, and Armenian co-owners, in order to ascertain the exact condition and the security of the edifice. Some three feet below the present pavement various mosaics of many colors and encased in beautiful and elaborate borders were uncovered. They date back to the time of the Emperor Constantine the Great (A.D. 272–337). These mosaics impart an added interest to the holiness of this shrine whose shadows are hallowed by the mystery of the first Christmas.

A SELECTED LIST OF PICTURES APPROPRIATE FOR CHRISTMAS

THE ANNUNCIATION

The Annunciation — Fra Angelico
The Annunciation — Sandro Botticelli

THE NATIVITY

Holy Night — Correggio
The Nativity — Hofmann
Nativity — Luini
Holy Night — Carl Muller
The Nativity — Sinkel
The Holy Family (3) — Chambers[1]
The Holy Family (5) — Chambers
The Nativity — Chambers
Noël — Chambers
The Divine Babe — Chambers

SHEPHERDS

Adoration of the Shepherds — Bougereau
Adoration of the Shepherds — Chambers
Arrival of the Shepherds — Lerolle
The Announcement — Plockhurst
The Shepherds at Bethlehem — Chambers
The Shepherds — Chambers

THE MAGI

Adoration of the Magi — Botticelli

---

[1] The works of C. Bosseron Chambers are obtainable from St. Anthony's Guild, Patterson, N. J.

Adoration of the Magi — Chambers
Adoration of the Magi — Durer
Worship of the Wise Men — Hofmann
The Wisemen — Chambers

FLIGHT INTO EGYPT

Repose in Egypt — Correggio
Flight into Egypt — Durer
Rest in Flight — Knaus
Repose in Egypt — Merson
Holy Family — Murillo
Flight in Egypt — Plockhurst
Repose in Egypt — Plockhurst
Holy Family — Reuben
Rest in Flight — Vandyck
Star of Bethlehem — Piglheim

MADONNAS

Madonna — Cimabue
Madonna — Giotto
Madonna — Fra Angelico
Madonna — Sandro Botticelli
Madonna — Carlo Dolci
Madonna — Ittenbach
Madonna and Child — Sichels
Madonna and Child — Ferruzzi
Madonna and Child — Bodenhausen
Madonna and Child — Giovanni Bellini
Madonna and Child — Leonardo da Vinci
Madonna and Child — Bernardino Luini
Madonna and Child — Dagnan Bouveret
Madonna and Child — Gabiel Max
Madonna of the Rabbit — Titian
Madonna of the Olive Branch — Barabino
Sistine Madonna — Raphael
Madonna of the Chair — Raphael

Madonna Granduca — Raphael
Madonna of the Goldfinch — Raphael
Madonna di Tempi — Raphael
Madonna della Tenda — Raphael
Madonna of the Harpies — Andrea Del Sarto
Mother and Child — Murillo
Mother and Child — Fra Filippo Lippi
Our Lady of the Angels — Bougereau
Mary with the Child — Dürer
Saint Mary — Ittenbach
Angels — Fra Angelico
Angels — Giovanni Bellini
The Christ Child — Ittenbach
Bambino — Della Robbia
Head of Christ — Murillo
Choir of Angels — Sir Joshua Reynolds
Christmas Chimes — Blashfield
The Eternal Babe — Chambers
Madonna and Child — Chambers
Gloria in Excelsis Deo — Chambers